BEAUTY GUIDE

Epilation Treatment

Beauty Guides by Ann Gallant

1 Muscle Contraction Treatment
2 Figure Treatment
3 Galvanic Treatment
4 Epilation Treatment

Also by Stanley Thornes (Publishers) Ltd

Joyce Allsworth	*Skin Camouflage: A Guide to Remedial Techniques*
Elaine Almond	*Safety in the Salon*
W E Arnould-Taylor	*The Principles and Practice of Physical Therapy*
W E Arnould-Taylor	*Aromatherapy for the Whole Person*
Ann Gallant	*Body Treatments and Dietetics for the Beauty Therapist*
Ann Gallant	*Principles and Techniques for the Electrologist*
Ann Gallant	*Principles and Techniques for the Beauty Specialist*
Ann Hagman	*The Aestheticienne*
John Rounce	*Science for the Beauty Therapist*

BEAUTY GUIDE 4

Epilation Treatment

Ann Gallant
F.S.H.B.Th., Int.B.Th.Dip., D.R.E. (Tutor),
Teacher's Certificate in Further Education

*Formerly Lecturer Responsible
for Beauty Therapy at
Chichester College of Higher Technology, and
Gloucestershire College of Art and Technology*

Stanley Thornes (Publishers) Ltd

First published in 1985 by
Stanley Thornes (Publishers) Ltd,
Old Station Drive,
Leckhampton,
CHELTENHAM GL53 0DN

British Library Cataloguing in Publication Data

Gallant, Ann
Epilation treatments. — (Beauty guide; 4)
1. Hair — Removal 2. Electrolysis
I. Title II. Series
617'.47 RL115.5

ISBN 0-85950-216-3

Typeset in 10/11 Garamond
by Tech-Set, Gateshead, Tyne & Wear.
Printed and bound in Great Britain
at The Bath Press, Avon.

Contents

ACKNOWLEDGEMENTS

My thanks go to my husband, Robin Cleugh, who worked with patience and skill to provide all the photographs in this practical guide — making it so much more usable to the beauty practitioner working in the field. Thanks also to Angela Lumley for her care in the line drawings and sympathetic approach to the subject. I'd like to record special thanks to my photographic models, including my daughter Patsy, who enabled us to get some of the special shots we needed for this practical guide, to help students with positioning and technique.

Introduction

Wherever the electrologist works, her task will be essentially the same — bringing about the permanent removal of unwanted hair without skin damage. Her work may be within an electrology practice, in medical surroundings, or more commonly in association with professional beauty therapy; but the people she treats will all need her help equally. They may be called clients, patrons, or patients depending on the status and position of professional electrology in the country where treatment is offered, and depending on under whose overall responsibility the work falls — whether the work is carried out in the medical or private sector.

ELECTROLOGIST AT WORK

Permanent hair removal may be accomplished in a number of ways, the most common being the epilation method, using frequencies known as *short wave diathermy.* Still available is the older galvanic chemical method, which preceded the epilation method and gave the title of *electrolysis* to permanent hair removal, by which it is still known by most of the general public. Other methods include the blend method, which uses both chemical and heat effects to produce hair destruction. Most advanced epilation systems use a mixture or combination of frequencies to produce maximum destruction with minimum skin reaction and discomfort for the client. These wave-shaping effects or modalities suppress the discomfort associated with short wave diathermy methods and improve treatment results dramatically. There are even computer-controlled machines available which can, with skill, be made to combine the very best frequency, timing and intensity to meet the client's special needs. So the choice of method is wide and only depends on the operator's skill and financial limits.

In most common use internationally is short wave diathermy epilation which is normally considered a fairly high-frequency system. It uses heat for its destructive effects on the hair. A new wave-shaping version of short wave diathermy epilation will be considered in this guide. It is designed for greater effectiveness in treatment with reduced discomfort and reaction for the client. This system has been expertly designed and tested to make work simple and allows the operator to concentrate on her client and her technique, not on her machine's controls. The new system eliminates the need for wave blending, the use of computers, or the use of galvanic current — all measures previously designed to help reduce pain and improve the effectiveness of treatment, thereby reducing regrowth potential for the client. However this new system is applied, for example, by manual finger control, foot control with automatic timing, etc., its effects remain constant, so the choice of control is the operator's. With excellent destructive effects, without associated skin damage or discomfort for the client, the electrologist will find her technique improving as she works with the new system. Being able to obtain improved results for the client is very worthwhile and the operator can now obtain equipment to match her own skill.

In many parts of the world, the study of professional electrology is either closely associated with beauty therapy within two-year college programmes, or can be studied independently for between 6 and 12 months. Training standards differ enormously around the world, with minimum hours of training varying from 200 to 1000 hours. Different examination boards set their own requirements for entry to examinations, and these standards are often used as guidelines by insurance companies when organizing professional insurance for electrologists.

Electrology can be successfully offered as a private practice, or work can be carried out in association with a beauty therapy clinic, medical practice, or a para-medical organization. In all cases, the electrologist will need to let her public know she is there and willing to help them, so as well as acquiring her skills she must also become a professional woman with business ability if she is to succeed.

In the United Kingdom, the client is only termed a patient when under direct medical supervision, otherwise the terms client, patron, etc., are more correct. If the electrologist completes her work under a doctor's direction within a hospital, then the person is termed a patient — but she is the doctor's patient, not the electrologist's. In the United States the situation is different, and electrology is separately organized from beauty work. Full beauty therapy with its health maintenance aspects is not well-established there as yet. Electrologists in the United States call themselves practitioners or professional electrologists, and refer to their

clients as patients. Every country approaches the situation differently because of differing standards of training, different licensing laws in operation in each country, different registration and health authority controls, etc. (See Chapter 11, 'Being Successful in the Business'.

Of prime importance in the electrologist's world are her clients who make learning a difficult and responsible skill worthwhile. Good skills, a caring attitude, and good equipment to complete the task are all important and play their part, but without the people who need the special skills, there is no profession.

1

Advances in treatment

The new frequency combinations of the latest epilation systems, such as the *Beauty Gallery* range, provide a breakthrough in the treatment of superfluous hair. Many clients experience up to a 40% reduction in pain, while getting desired results. The new system has been developed to destroy gently the follicles' capacity to generate new hairs, but at the same time to complete this without skin damage. This epilation system provides excellent results when used correctly, but it does require accuracy on the part of the operator. The normal angry and painful reactions on the skin associated with the traditional short wave diathermy epilation machines do not occur with this new advanced system when applied correctly. Erythema (skin reddening), swelling and inflamed skin reactions are kept to a minimum, making skin healing a quicker process and avoiding skin marking or scarring, thereby allowing treatment overall to progress more quickly.

Although the hairs are removed gently, the hairs are destroyed just as effectively as before. What is different is that the skin and client suffer less — a good point in building up epilation customers. The pain reduction factor encourages many more people to benefit from epilation treatment, and those who were previously contra-indicated through skin sensitivity or low pain capacity can now cope easily with this new treatment.

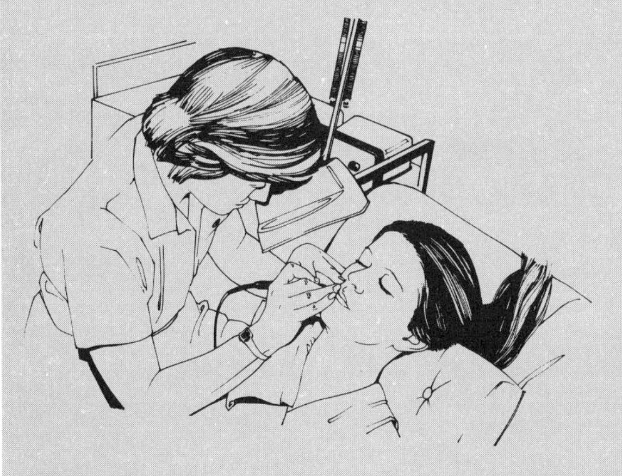

WORKING POSITION FOR FACIAL EPILATION

To gain full benefit from these advances in equipment, it is important to adopt a new approach to treatment. The client's skin will not show such obvious signs of current application, as the current is discharged using frequencies which are much kinder on the skin. There is no 'heat explosion' effect inside the follicle to affect the skin and cause painful surface reactions, inflammation, etc. Instead, a steady discharge of current destroys the root, loosens the hair from the follicle and cuts off its blood supply, so restricting its regrowth potential.

'BEAUTY GALLERY' UNIT COMPLETE WITH EPILATION SYSTEM

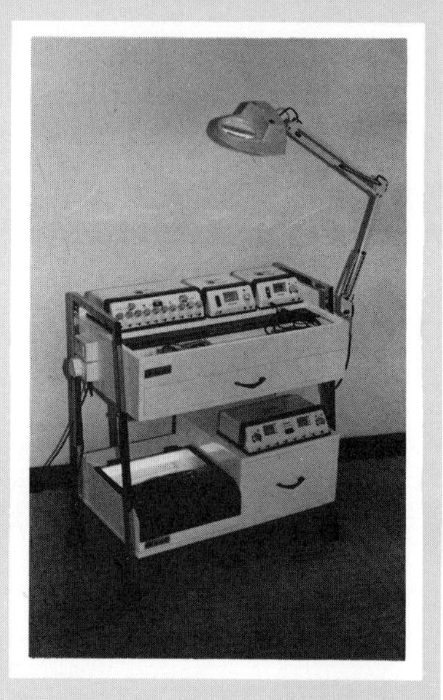

With the *Beauty Gallery* epilation system, most facial hairs can be epilated easily on an intensity of 2 to 4; very fine, dense, upper-lip hairs in fact often need less, as little as 1½ to 2. Stronger chin hairs may need intensities of between 3 and 5 or less if of a downy nature. Leg hairs will require anything from 4 to 7 depending on

EPILATION UNIT, NEEDLE HOLDER AND NEEDLES

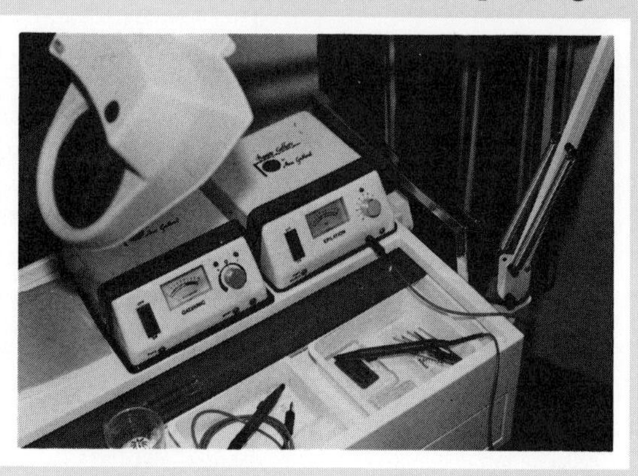

the strength of hairs. The rule of using the least possible current to effect a removal, working up from the minimum intensity until the current level is found to remove the hair successfully, still holds good even with the very advanced systems currently available.

NEED FOR ACCURACY

As the heat explosion effect is not present on the surface of the skin with this improved system, operators must judge the amount of current needed by their actual removals. As hairs are removed initially, they should be inspected carefully to judge their depth in the skin, strength, texture and hair root formation. This check indicates the amount of current needed, and the depth of needle probe. Probing too deeply is the main reason why hairs do not come out correctly. Fractionally over-shooting the base of the follicle, or discharging current too close to the surface skin — placing the active current below or above the correct matrix area of the hair root — are both common faults which produce ineffective removals and unnecessary skin damage.

CORRECTLY EPILATED HAIRS WITH TISSUE SHEATHS INTACT

Accuracy is especially critical if insulated steel needles are used as the concentration of current occurs at the tip of the needle, *so this must reach the matrix area of the hair root for the destruction to take place.* When this is carried out accurately, the result is excellent and minimizes skin damage and pain even further. However, if the current is not placed *exactly* in the right place, the hair root will not be destroyed — the hair will not come free from the follicle and will appear to need more intensity. The natural temptation in this situation is to increase the intensity of the current, believing it to be insufficient, but this is often quite wrong. Accuracy and technique are usually at fault, not lack of power — it is more a question of putting the power in the right place, so probe depth, angle of probe, skin-holding, positioning, and stretching should all

be checked carefully before any increase in intensity is given. If the operator feels (using this new unit) that she is using adequate levels of intensity and yet does not achieve effective removals, she must check through these points very carefully. All the advances in equipment, new frequencies, new needles, etc., designed to aid the operator in her task, can have little impact if the work itself is not accurate. The equipment is only as good as the operator's skill.

LATEST EPILATION SYSTEM WITH REDUCED DISCOMFORT

If one of the latest advanced systems is considered, such as the *Beauty Gallery* epilation unit, its details and advantages will provide a guide to what is needed in a successful system. It is a fully transistorized, solid-state electronic epilation unit, with simple, easy-to-understand controls and a meter to record accurately the actual power transmitted. This allows very accurate treatment records to be kept for individual clients. The unit incorporates a 'switch control' needle holder which greatly extends the working life of the electronic components, as they only operate while the switch button is depressed.

EPILATION UNIT

Simple and effective controls

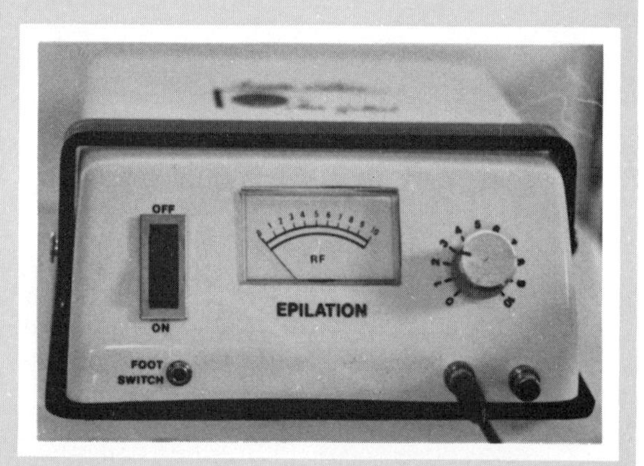

The *Beauty Gallery* epilation units provide for both manual and automatic timing (with the addition of a plain needle holder and foot switch). Two needle-holder outlets are provided on the units. This allows the operator to change her method of working to suit the particular treatment. The foot switch can be timed manually or used automatically (on the Auto Model) with the time and intensity set by the operator and applied automatically at the touch of the foot switch. The finger switch needle holder is only used manually, giving total control to the operator, allowing her to choose the exact current strength and length of application for each individual hair.

POWER CONTROL/SAFETY FEATURES

With the modern electronic epilation units, fluctuations in power cannot occur as the current is stabilized inside the unit; what the operator chooses, she gets from her machine. So when an intensity is chosen, used and recorded on the client's record card, it can be duplicated on subsequent treatments. This control of the power intensity prevents accidents happening and is a great advance on the older style of equipment which was not transistorized. There is also no need with the *Beauty Gallery* epilation unit to worry about whether power is flowing through to the needle tip correctly. With the new switch control of the needle holder, the power is either on or off, according to whether the switch is depressed or released. The connection is made electronically inside the needle holder, which is a great improvement on working safety. A red light indicates when power is flowing to the needle holder.

With the switch control system the current is instantly cut off as the finger is lifted from the switch — the connection is broken electronically — and this helps prevent current flowing while the operator is withdrawing the needle from the follicle, which could otherwise cause surface burns to occur. All these points are related to errors in technique and should not occur, but these extra safeguards provide additional protection for the client.

NEEDLE HOLDER

The unit is supplied with a switch control needle holder, and has outlets for a spare needle holder and for foot switch controls. If required, the foot switch and matching plain needle holder are available as optional extras. Extra finger-type needle holders are also available separately, as it is useful to have a spare when working fast (as different diameter needles can be used in either

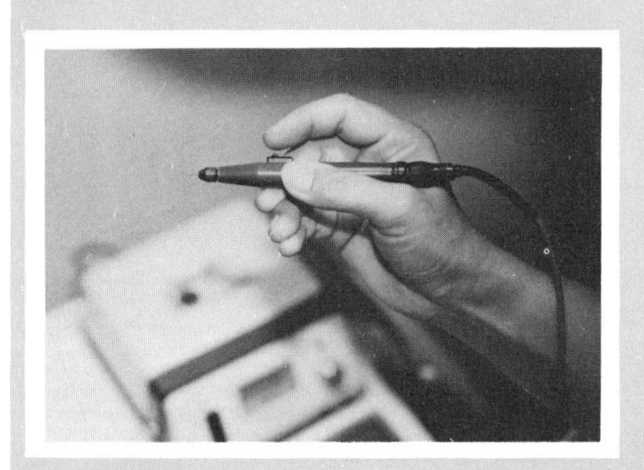

LATEST SWITCH CONTROL NEEDLE HOLDER

holder, allowing changes from coarse to very fine hairs to be accomplished swiftly, without interrupting the flow of treatment). Only the latest switch control needle holders can be used with the *Beauty Gallery* epilation unit (finger method) as they are custom made to suit the frequencies of this particular unit.

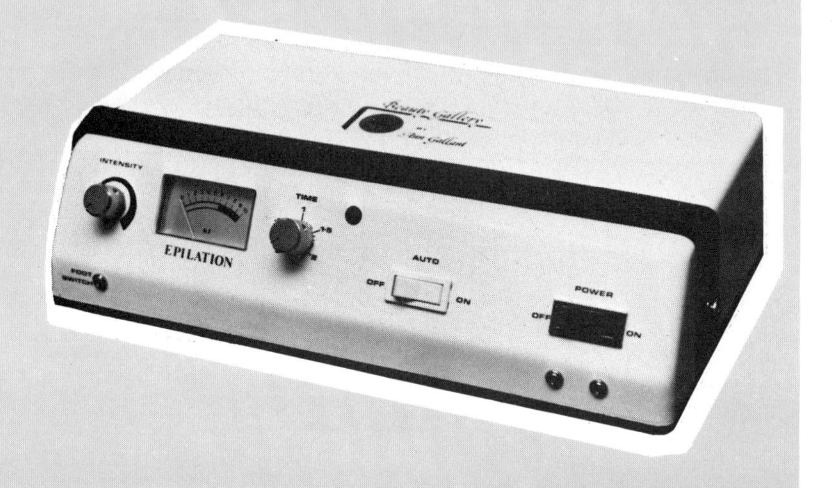

2

How epilation works

Epilation works by introducing an electrical current accurately to the active base of the hair follicle by means of a fine metal probe or needle. The skin tissues react against this electrical current and heat is produced which causes the hair to become detached within the follicle or hair pocket. The follicle's ability to generate a new hair is considerably reduced or curtailed. The blood supply to the follicle is cut off by the short wave diathermy current, so that it can neither sustain another hair nor receive hormone messages via the blood circulation from the body's endocrine system which affects overall hair growth.

For this to happen, however, the current has to be placed accurately at the base of the hair follicle, at the *active matrix* area. This is an area of great mitotic activity (cellular division) and has at its centre the *dermal papilla,* where the strength, shape, colour and life span of the hair starts to be determined. Sufficient short wave diathermy 'heat' current has to be applied to this matrix area for a hair to be lifted free from the follicle without resistance. Achieving this without unnecessary associated skin damage is the art of successful epilation treatment.

If the skin structure is looked at, it can be seen that hairs lie at different angles in the skin and the follicles are at different depths in the surface tissues. Follicles are lined throughout by surface epidermal tissue but the hairs lie within the deeper dermis, from which they receive their nutrition and basic life support. Through hormone messages (chemical catalysts) circulating in the blood, they also receive information that determines their growth potential.

HEALTH AND HAIR GROWTH

Hair growth is directly controlled by the endocrine system, and hair can be considered as an 'end organ' of the endocrine system because it reacts to minute hormone changes in the body. This is most noticeable in puberty, pregnancy and during the menopause — all natural stages of life where the body's hormone balance is erratic, over-active or diminishing. Illness, general poor health or abnormalities of the endocrine system, such as over-activity of the

SKIN STRUCTURE

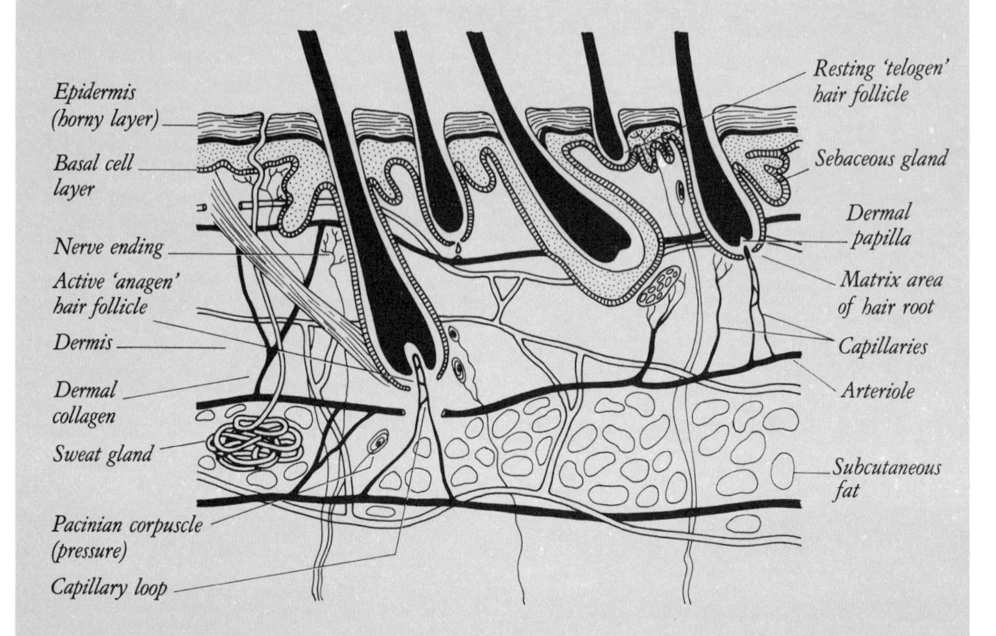

thyroid gland, can also cause hair changes to occur; the facial hair appears to be especially sensitive to these tiny hormone alterations. (For further information on causes of unwanted hair growth and its relationship to the endocrine system, see *Principles and Techniques for the Electrologist,* by Ann Gallant.)

HAIR GROWTH CYCLE

Hairs have a very organized pattern of growth and replacement known as the *hair growth cycle.* In a healthy person, hair replacement exactly matches hair shed; fine new hairs are often visible while the old established hairs are in the process of being lost. A fine hair and a thick hair can often be seen emerging from the same follicle, especially on the leg areas where growth tends to be stronger.

During ill health, replacement hairs may not grow and there can be a hair loss, patchy growth or thinning of hair on the head, in men and women. Typical male baldness is under the direct control of hormone and sexual influences, and demonstrates clearly that very few external influences can affect hair growth potential, rather it is internal factors which determine the growth pattern.

Hairs are said to go through a pattern or cycle of hair growth known as the *anagen, catagen,* and *telogen* stages, which simply means the growing, transition or changing, and resting stages. The purpose

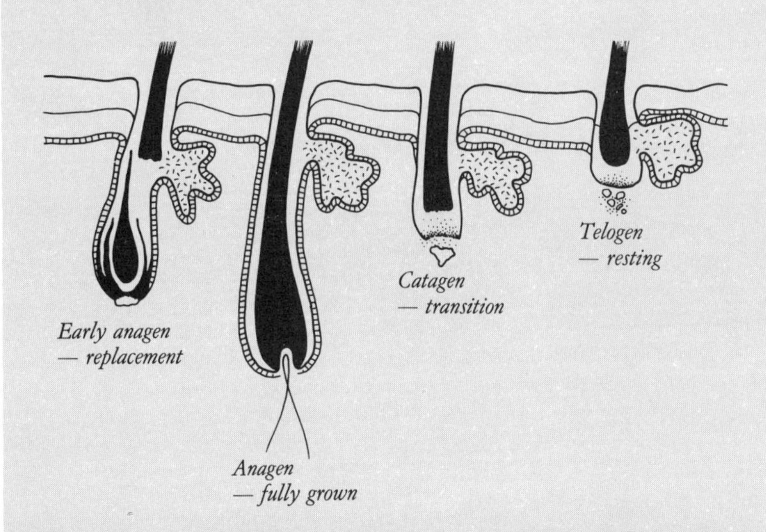

of the cycle is to ensure that the amount of hair present stays constant. This hair growth cycle is important to successful epilation practice; if the active area of the hair root is not reached accurately by the tip of the needle probe, the hair will not be effectively destroyed.

3

Points of technique

POSITIONING AND PROBING

The operator must match her probe exactly to the depth and angle of each individual follicle, using her sense of touch to determine correctly the position and depth at which the hair lies. A close look at initial removals, to see the shape and strength and depth of tissue sheath surrounding the hair itself at its root, also helps the assessment. Matching the angle of the insertion to the angle at which the hair leaves the follicle is also essential for fast, comfortable probes. If the needle probe and hair follicle are exactly matched to each other, the needle will enter the follicle easily with

PROBING AND ADJUSTING THE CURRENT

(a) Judging the depth of follicle and current intensity needed after inspection of initial removals

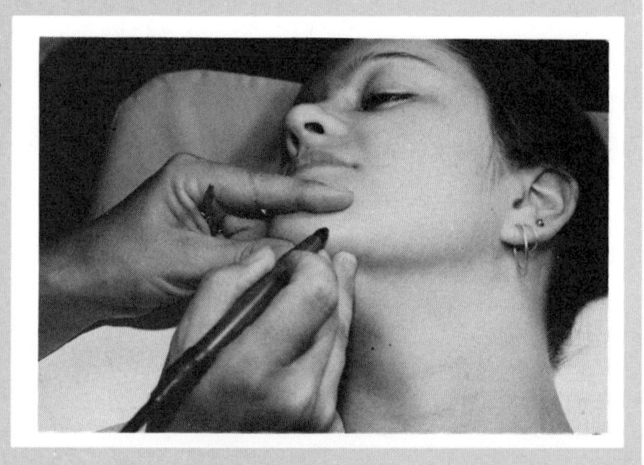

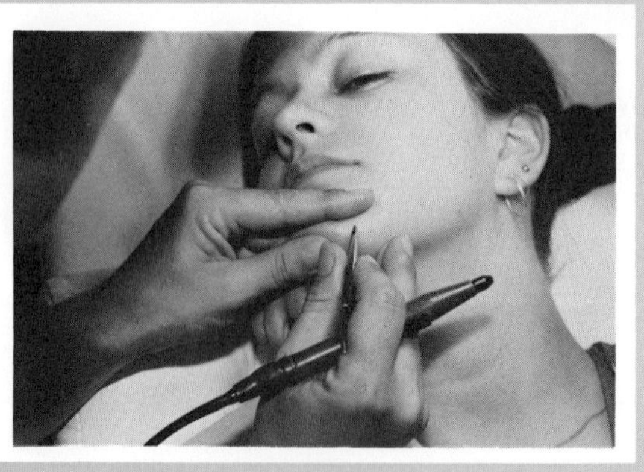

(b) The hair should come free without resistance and with the tissue sheath intact

no resistance from the skin or discomfort for the client, and the operator will know she has made a correct insertion. Now all that remains is to 'judge' the depth correctly and assess the correct amount of current intensity needed to bring about a successful removal.

ANAGEN STAGE

Hairs at the *anagen* stage of the growth cycle are at their strongest and deepest and have the best blood supply of any stage of the growth pattern, so these probes will be deeper and will require fractionally more current intensity to achieve a satisfactory removal and destruction. Anagen hairs regrow more frequently than catagen or telogen hairs. The skin often acts as the limiting factor to how much current intensity can be applied, and if the skin is sensitive and the hair very strong, then the current chosen must relate to the skin capacity, rather than the needs of the hair. So the hair may regrow in a weaker more shallow form and its destruction will have to be completed on a second or even third regrowth occasion. *Remember: the greater your probing accuracy, the less regrowth that occurs.*

CATAGEN STAGE

Catagen hairs are shorter in the follicle, have not got such a well-formed tissue sheath or root structure, and do not have such a good blood supply to sustain their growth. This is because they are progressing towards the resting stage in the cycle, their period of life is over, their cellular activity at the hair root is diminished. These hairs will require more superficial probes, using less intensity of current, and care will be necessary to avoid the danger of surface burns. Regrowth potential is reduced as the hair is not in an active growing stage, and the follicle is preparing to rest rather than form a new hair.

TELOGEN STAGE

Telogen hairs are very superficial in the skin and have a club-like root structure, with all mitotic activity over for the present. The hair follicle is resting and in time the hair will actually be shed. Telogen hairs require very little current intensity to remove, but it must be carefully applied to avoid surface burns, pitting, dehydration and scarring. A careful, steady touch, low intensity, and a rather upright probe angle are often the best means of treatment. No regrowth can occur if the hair has been correctly epilated, as treatment at this stage of the hair growth cycle catches the follicle at its weakest moment and only a tiny amount of short wave diathermy current is needed to destroy the follicle's capacity to form a new hair.

(c) Work upwards from the minimum current intensity until an ideal level is reached

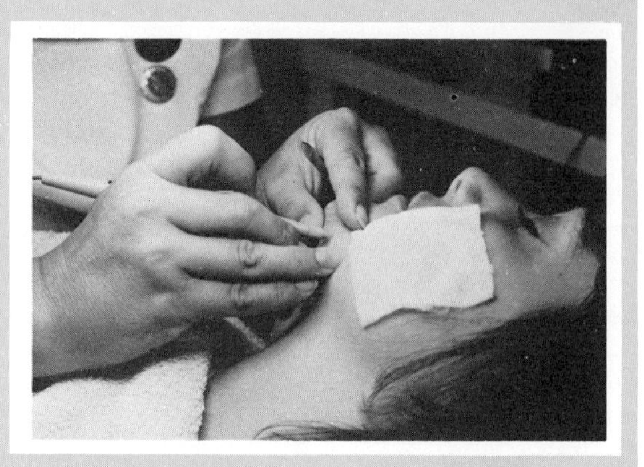

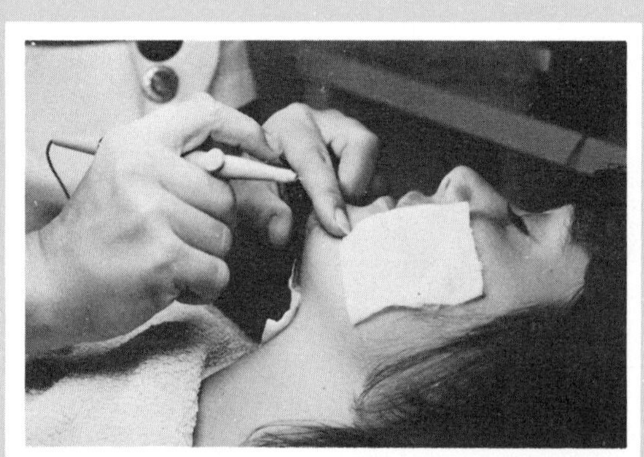

(d), (e) Remember, skin sensitivity always determines how much current can be used

(e)

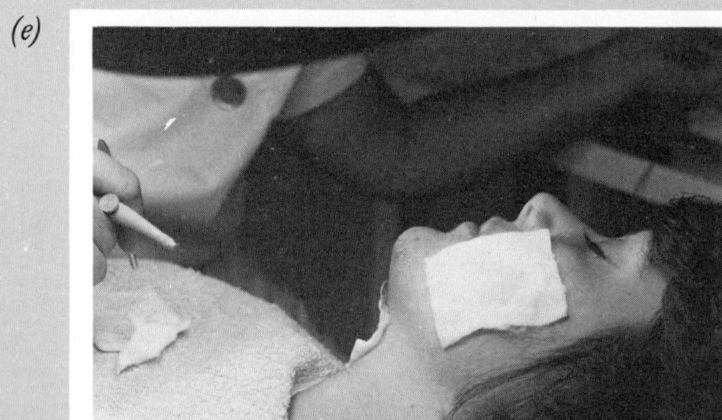

As all these hair stages can be intermingled in any one area of treatment such as the face, the operator has to make constant decisions — about the amount of intensity needed — the depth of the probe — the angle of the needle insertion — how much current

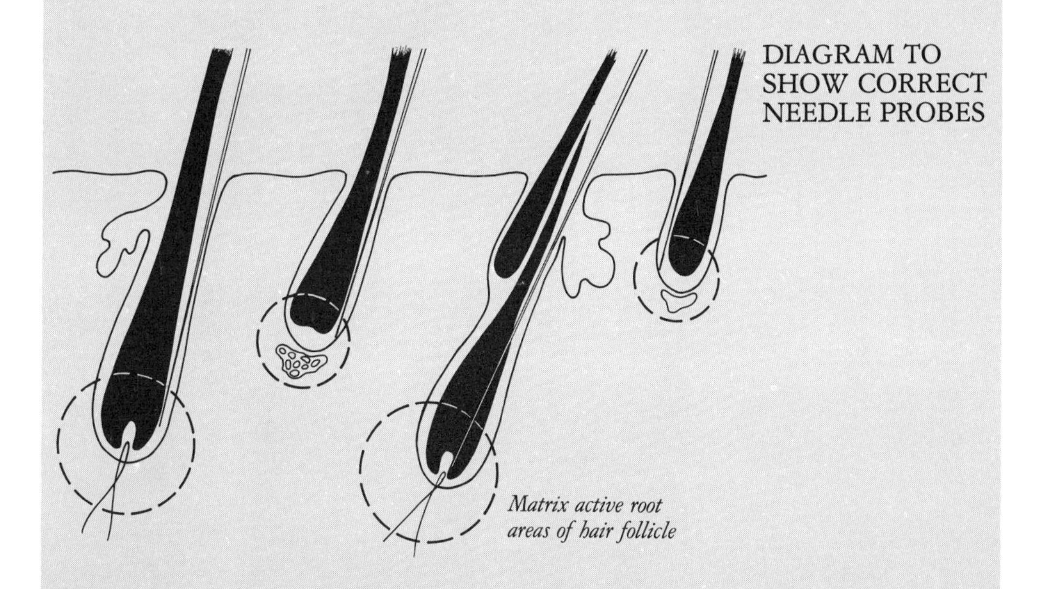

the skin can stand, etc. Looking at the diameter and type of hairs present at the initial skin inspection prior to treatment will help to decide the stage of hair growth that dominates. Just as regrowth hairs can be easily identified when they emerge, strong anagen-type hairs are also fairly easy to recognize. Strong hairs present from some hormone or health irregularity may be difficult to judge accurately prior to actual removal, but ordinary 'cosmetic' unwanted hairs on a normal healthy person have certain basic characteristics which the operator soon learns to recognize.

By understanding how the hair growth cycle works in a normal healthy person, it is possible to see what happens when it is altered by hormone influence from within the body. The follicle is capable of growing deeper and stronger, and finding itself a better blood supply to help it become a more active growing unit. So strong superfluous hairs can grow where previously there has been only fine, downy, vellus-type hair. The follicle can change its role to grow stronger hairs if sent the right messages via the blood stream from the endocrine system. Accurate epilation destroys the follicle's capacity to form and sustain a hair as well as removing the hair present.

TREATING STRONG HAIRS

(a) Where hair growth is strong and mixed in type, use a moderate level of intensity and a medium diameter needle. Adjust the current application by careful finger control on the switch

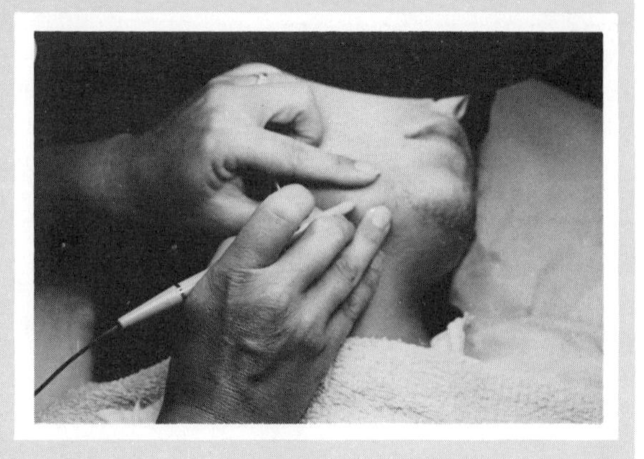

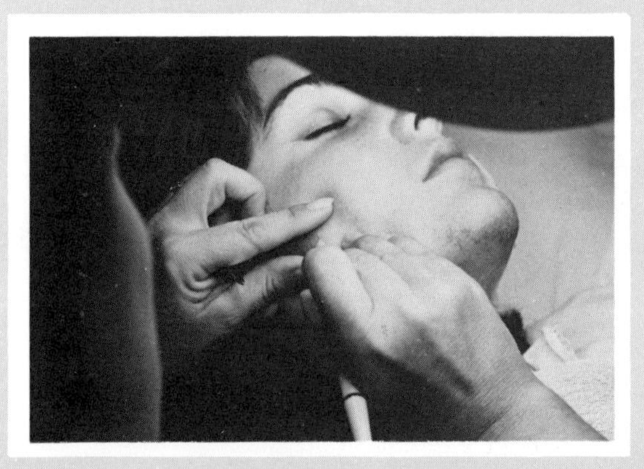

(b) With strong, deeply rooted hairs, work slowly and carefully to maximize effect and minimize regrowth potential

(c) Hairs concentrated into clumps on the side of the chin must be treated with well-spaced probes to avoid converging heat reactions which slow healing

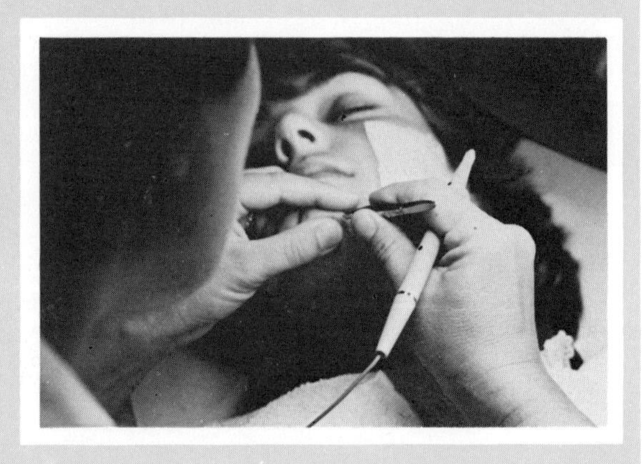

SENSE OF TOUCH

The operator can also use her *sense of touch* to guide her probes, feeling through her hands when resistance occurs at the tip of the needle. If lightness of touch and a careful approach are used, in time it will be possible to sense when the needle tip has reached the correct place at the base of the follicle. Any resistance to the needle may either indicate that the base of the follicle has been reached or that the angle of the probe has caused the side of the follicle wall to be touched, or the needle tip has entered the sebaceous gland opening, giving a false impression of having reached the root area. Repositioning will sort out many probing errors of this type. It is important to *match exactly the angle of the hair coming out of the follicle, with the angle of the needle being inserted.* Failure to do this will lead to poor results and slow painful work for the client. The operator must move her client to where she needs her to be for successful probing, moving her head into a good position, and also using her fingers to position and hold the skin in such a way that the epilation can be completed efficiently and insertions can be achieved with ease. Clients like to feel gently but firmly

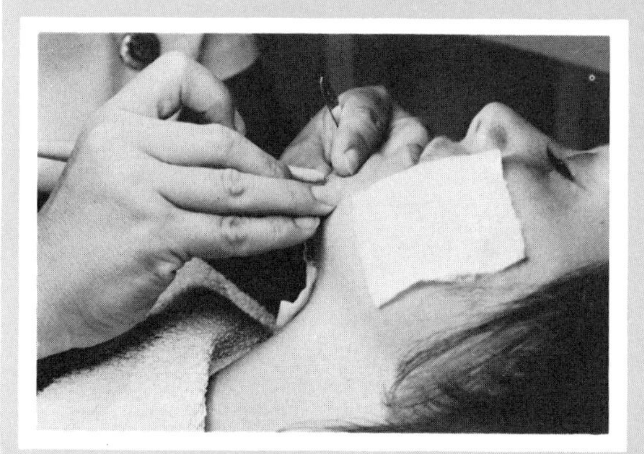

SENSE OF TOUCH

(a) Firm but gentle handling of the skin develops a sense of touch which guides the operator as to the depth and angle of probe

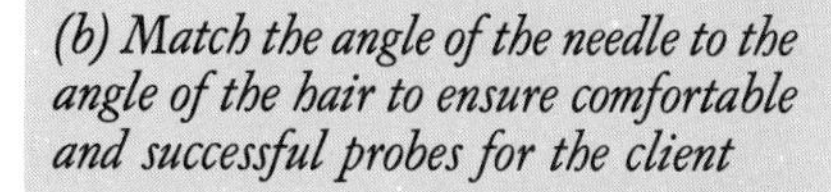

(b) Match the angle of the needle to the angle of the hair to ensure comfortable and successful probes for the client

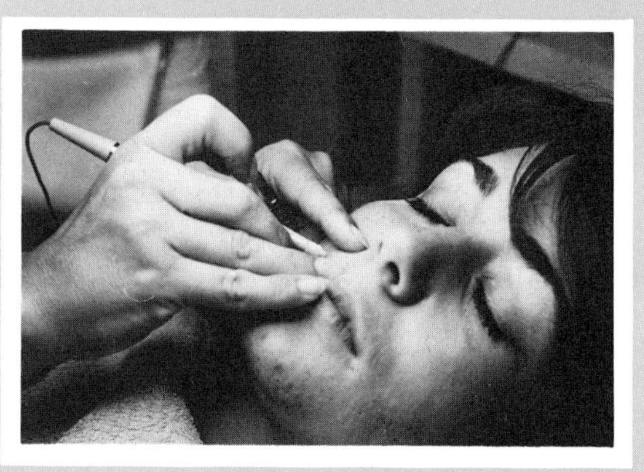

guided into position, and feel reassured if they are treated by an operator with a comforting sense of touch. So never be afraid to put the client where you want her; if it helps the work to be completed well, it is helping the client to obtain the best results overall.

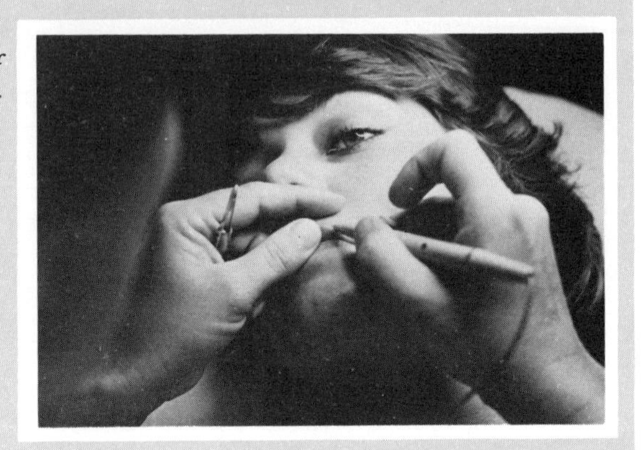

(c) If any resistance is felt on the probe, it can indicate that the angle of insertion is wrong, or skin control is poor and must be corrected

ACCURACY IN TREATMENT

The need for accuracy in treatment is to ensure successful hair removals, but it also has other advantages. If a hair is removed accurately there will be less skin damage, regrowth will be minimized, and the skin will heal more rapidly, speeding the overall progress of the treatment plan. There will be less risk of skin dehydration, pitting, scarring, and pigmentation changes occurring, which often occurs as a result of putting the current in the wrong place in relation to the hair root. The skin reacts to this inaccuracy with skin trauma, inflammation, irritation, and swelling. Probing the follicle too deeply — over-shooting the follicle base — is the commonest cause of both poor removals and permanent skin damage, as excessive current is often used to compensate for inaccuracy. The hairs are blasted out of the follicles, and the whole skin area becomes damaged in the process. When resistance is felt at the tip of the needle, however slight, this must not be ignored and overcome with extra pressure, for it indicates the active matrix area of the follicle has been reached. Hairs epilated accurately will lift from the follicle with no resistance. To see how superficial in the skin hairs really are, it is a good idea for operators to measure an epilated hair against the length of the needle itself to get an actual, rather than an assumed idea of its depth. If even a very strong hair only relates to half the length of the needles in common use, such as the Ferrie steel and the insulated steel needles, then clearly that is all the probe depth required. To go deeper is to go right through the base of the follicle with the

sharp tip of the needle. Most follicles are much shallower than this, requiring only a small percentage of the needle to be inserted. The rounded probe insulated steel needles have their tips slightly rounded to prevent this occurrence, which is helpful, but really the operator must be aware of her own technique, and build up her own accuracy through touch, observation and working experience to avoid these errors.

One of the main reasons for accuracy in epilation treatment is that if the removals are not satisfactory, not only is the client disappointed because of poor progress, but hair regrowth will be excessive and she will lose faith in the treatment. Worries over scarring from treatment have prevented many people from seeking professional help in the past. These days, accuracy combined with the new frequencies available — such as with the *Beauty Gallery* epilation unit — should eliminate these fears, and allow more people to benefit from treatment.

ACCURACY AND CONTROL

(a) Epilation of upper-lip hair demands accuracy, control and a developed sense of touch

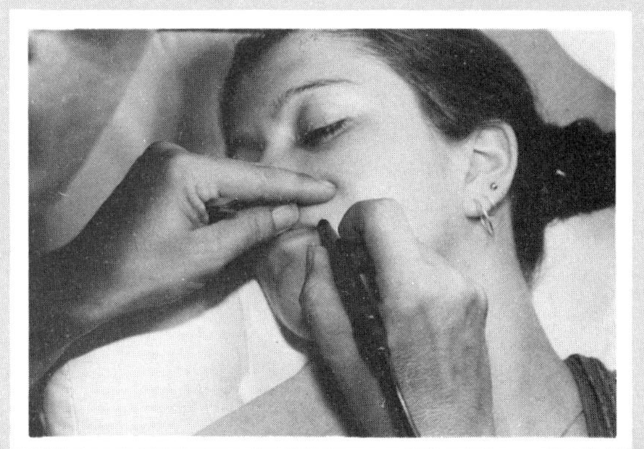

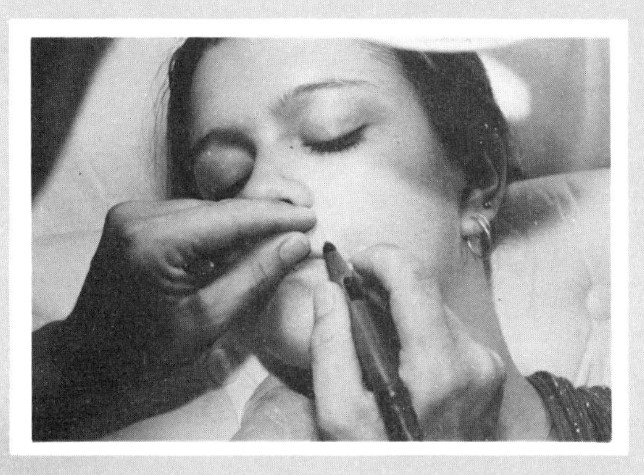

(b) Good control of the skin allows the current to be effective without the risk of superficial burns. The skin can be stretched, bunched or steadied to make the probe easier to achieve

(c) Achieving a correct probing angle becomes critical on the sensitive centre lip area

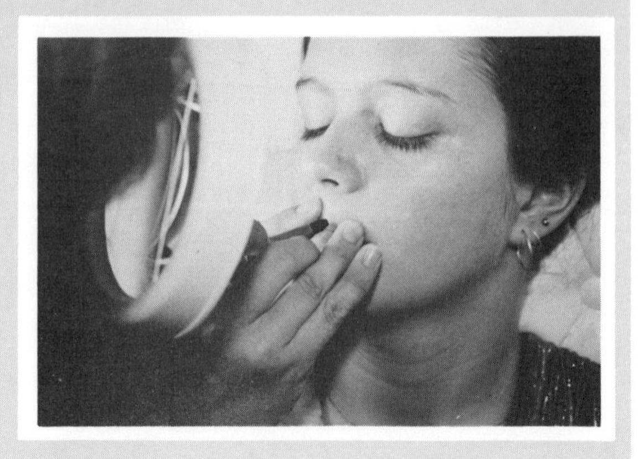

ANGLE AND PROBE DEPTH MUST RELATE CLOSELY TO THE HAIR ITSELF
(a), (b), (c), (d), (e), (f), (g)

(b)

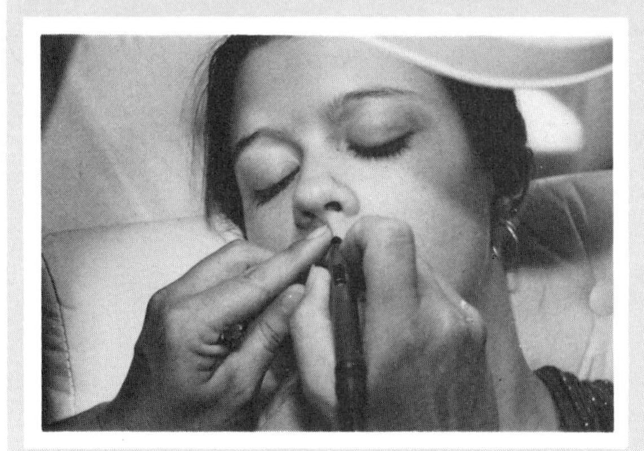

(c)

(d)

(e)

(f)

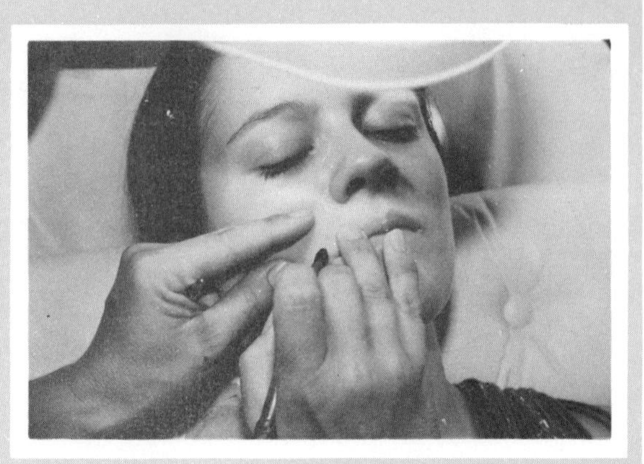

(g)

CONTROL OF THE SKIN

An essential part of technique is good control of the skin, using the fingers and thumbs to stretch and steady the skin in the treatment area. This provides a good base to position the needle holder and allows the needle to probe the follicle correctly. By giving the hands some support, a steadiness of hand is achieved which allows a comfortable needle insertion to be possible, and allows the current chosen and applied to reach the active area of the follicle accurately. This steadiness prevents loss of current into the surrounding tissues, cutting down needle movement at the moment of current application. Current 'spillage' not only causes poor reactions, but can result in ineffective removals as insufficient current remains in the hair root area to do its work of destruction. So the hair remains firmly attached to the follicle.

From practice on simple body hairs (normal hairs such as those found on the lower legs), the technique of good skin holding and stretching can be developed. This makes such a difference when

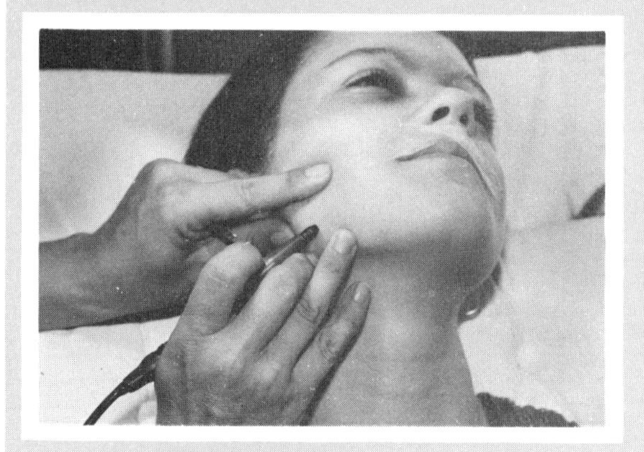

CONTROLLING THE SKIN

(a) Roll or bunch the skin to achieve a satisfactory probe in a difficult soft area

(b) Drop the client's head back on the multi-positional chair to bring the treatment area into the ideal position for work

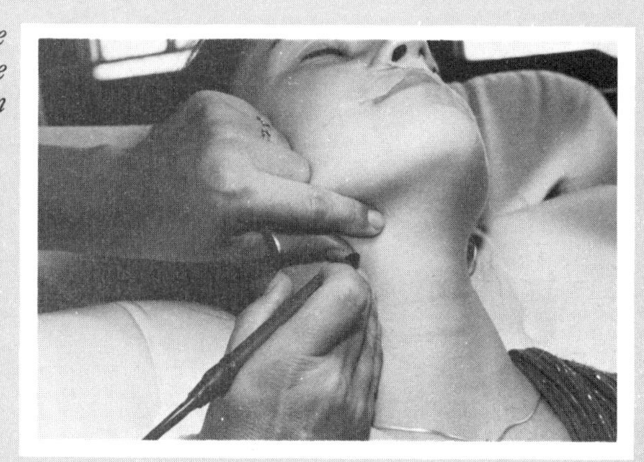

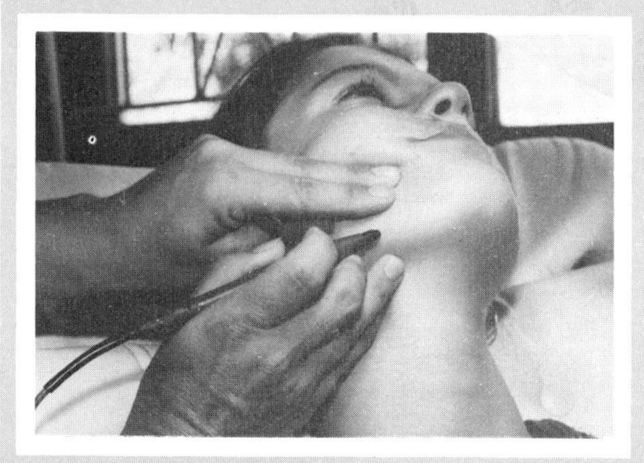

(c) Use the jawbone to support the hands while rolling the skin to achieve the probe

DEVELOPMENT OF TECHNIQUE

(a)–(c) Practice difficult hand movements on the legs, such as stretching, rolling and bunching the skin, as they must be mastered before progressing to the more difficult facial work

(a)

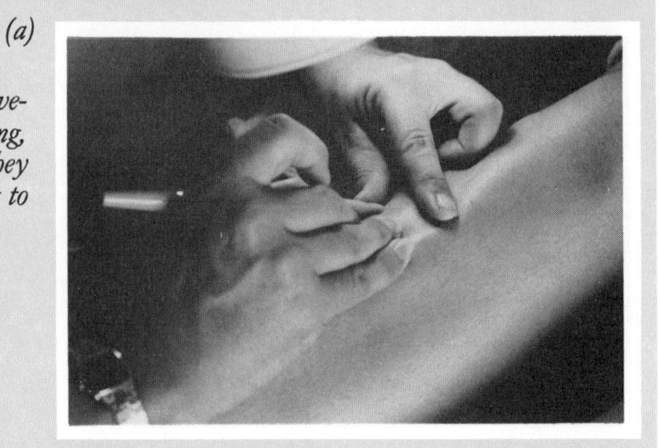

(b)

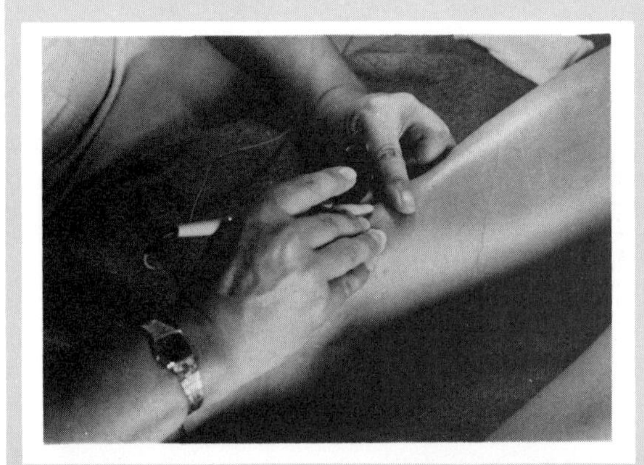

(c)

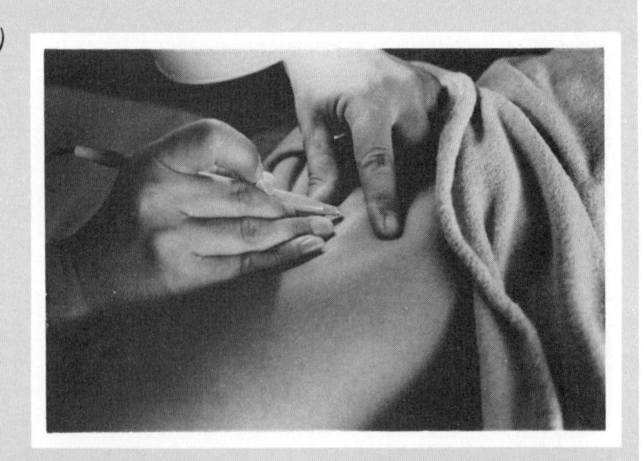

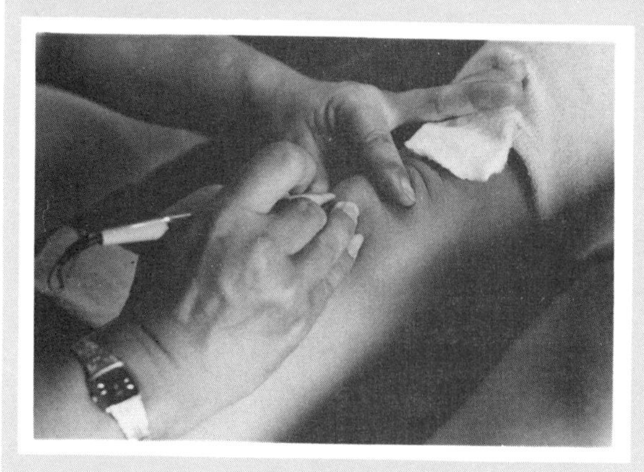

(d) Practice controlling the needle holder and forceps in these easier areas

(e), (f) Faults which occur at this stage, such as white ringing, can be cured before attempting facial work where scarring could result

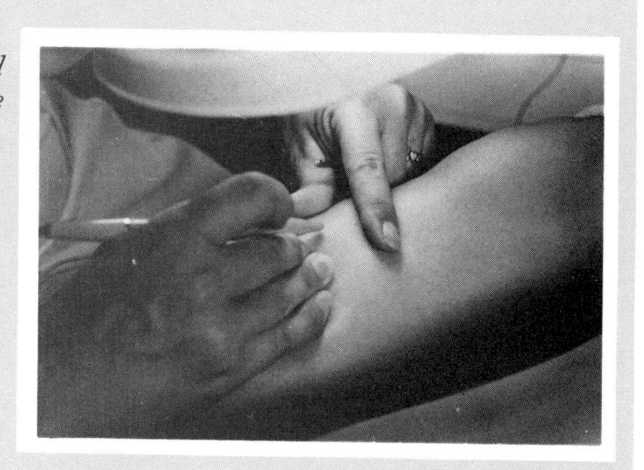

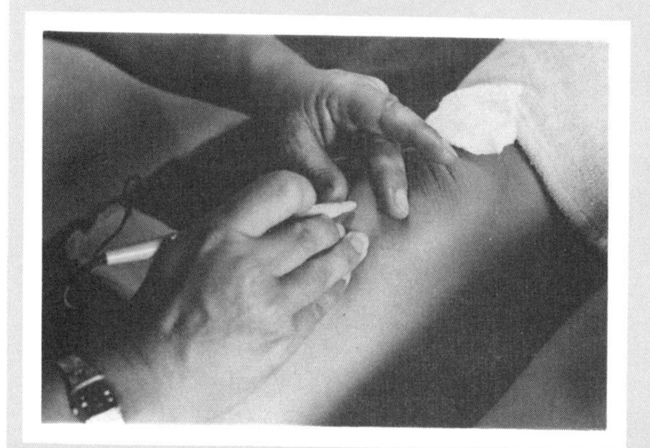

(f)

really difficult probes are being tackled on the face, and where more discomfort is normally associated with the application. The operator needs to be able to concentrate her full attention on the probes being accomplished and on the control of the current, etc., and must not still be trying to cope with holding her small tools correctly (needle holder and forceps), and attempting to hold the skin steady and stretched. These techniques *must* be mastered before approaching epilation work on the face, for the client's sake, if not for your own business reputation.

The skin can be handled in a variety of ways: stretching out, holding steady, lifting into the correct angle for an easy insertion, bunching it to help a probe to be accomplished on a difficult area, etc. All fingers available, as well as thumbs, can be used to help the skin positioning; control of the skin is especially important on difficult areas such as the neck, along the jaw, under the nose, etc. With gentle but firm skin control, the epilation can be completed far more quickly, as the follicle is placed in an ideal position to be probed. The client's head may need to be repositioned on the headrest if not angled correctly for the probe, and this can be done with a few sure movements of the hands. Minute adjustments, to speed and aid the probe, can be accomplished with the fingers, bringing the area of treatment to the correct working angle. With good finger control, the forceps can also be brought easily into the correct position to remove the dead treated hair, and then returned to their normal position after placing the epilated hair on a nearby cotton-wool pad. This smooth change-over of the hands and comfortable ease with the small tools comes from long practice, but should be mastered before attempting to work in the restricted area of the lip and chin where the space available between the magnifier and the client is limited. Each hand movement must be purposeful and careful, but has to be accomplished swiftly to ensure adequate treatment is accomplished in the client's appointment time.

FIRM SKIN CONTROL

(a) The skin can be stretched firmly along the jawbone to aid insertions in this difficult area

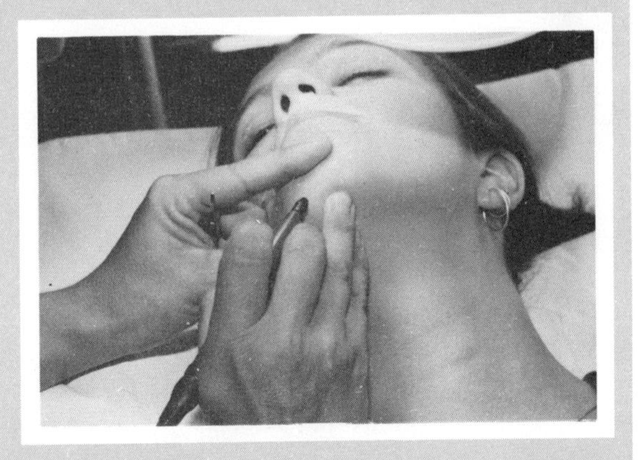

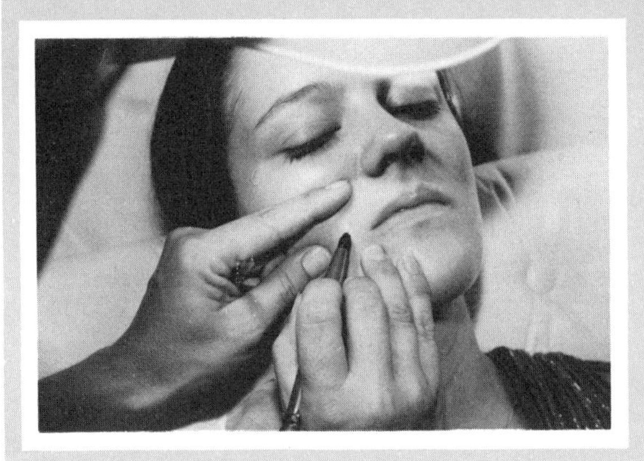

(b) Move the client's head if necessary to a position where accurate probe angles can be achieved

(c) A combination of pulling and stretching the skin between the two sets of fingers and thumbs brings a difficult probe area, such as the chin fold, into the correct position for an easy and accurate insertion

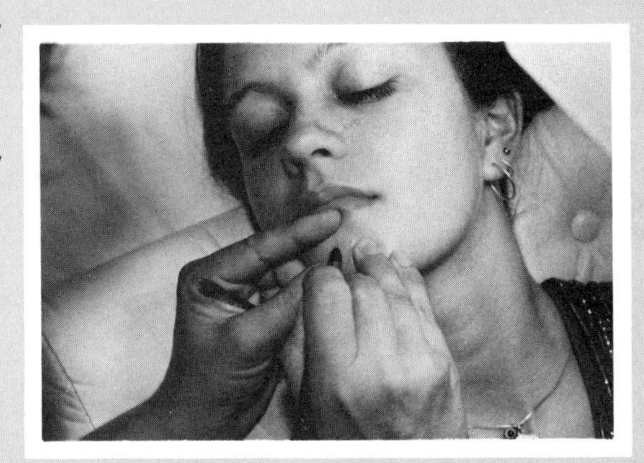

CHOICE OF CURRENT

The choice of current depends entirely on the operator's assessment of the hair, its strength, and most of all the skin's capacity to bear the epilation process. With the *Beauty Gallery* epilation system, much less intensity of current is required (when used accurately) to accomplish successful hair removal. So operators must adopt a new approach when working with this system, in order to gain from its advantages. Epilation may be applied working up from the minimum amount of intensity considered suitable, progressing upwards slowly in power until the correct level is reached, which achieves hair destruction effectively without undue skin damage or reaction. The rule is: use the minimum power possible to remove the hair without resistance. Initial probes can be applied once or twice, if the hair when touched with the forceps offers resistance and needs extra treatment to finish it off well. Hairs can be reprobed and current reapplied if the follicles and skin are not showing too much sign of treatment. The pattern

for the current intensity emerges from these early removals and provides guidance for subsequent hairs of a similar diameter and position. The current intensity can be adjusted on the epilation machine or it can be applied for fractionally longer on the switch control on the needle holder or with the foot switch — whichever suits the client and her skin/hair best.

By working slowly upwards in power the operator knows she is using the minimum required for the task, which cuts down skin reaction while maintaining good removals. This same approach is necessary for all treatment of superfluous hair growth, from fine downy hair from normal sources through to abnormal growth which is present as a result of hormone influences in the body. Using only the current required and using it accurately, is one of the basic points of technique. Most operators prefer to use a modest amount of current intensity, applied for a fraction of a second, to minimize pain and skin damage for the client. With the *Beauty Gallery* epilation system the machine automatically cuts off the current after two seconds, even if the finger is not lifted from the finger switch control, as it is considered excessive for the current to be applied for this duration; most hairs require only a fraction of a second with this new system and its effective frequencies. This safety function is *not* an automatic timer — the operator is the only person who can decide the duration and intensity of current needed to epilate a hair successfully — it is simply an automatic cut-out which prevents misuse of the current through error or inexperience. The epilation unit is however available with an automatic timer and foot switch if preferred.

MANUAL OR AUTOMATIC CONTROL

The electrologist has the choice of manual or automatic timing methods, and can use the method she prefers, and according to the work being undertaken. Choice will depend to a large extent on the training received, and which method is in most general use in the operator's country of work. It is useful to be competent in both methods of work, as this increases the employment range internationally. Good results can be obtained whichever method is employed, if the operator has regard for basic technique, and matches the hair's strength against the current strength and length of application accurately.

Manual control, either on the switched needle holder or via the foot switch, gives total control to the electrologist, as she decides the exact amount of current needed for each individual hair. She can change the amount of current used instantly, by prolonging the application of the current fractionally (prolonging the tap) to meet the exact needs of the hair for perfect destruction. Finger switch or foot switch methods work equally well, giving instant

connection of current and excellent control. When the foot switch is in use it automatically cuts out the finger switch needle holder from being operative, and a plain needle holder is used — with no switch. For this reason two needle-holder outlets are built into the *Beauty Gallery* epilation unit, allowing a fast change from one method to the other to be possible, or to provide for two switched needle holders to be always available for the operator's convenience. These can hold different diameter needles if required.

With the foot switch method, automatic timing is also available for operators who prefer it, or feel it speeds their work. Once switched to the automatic method, and with the intensity and length of application set by the operator, touching the foot switch sets off the current, which is then discharged automatically. It is identical every time, until altered by the operator to meet the changing nature of the hairs being treated. As long as the hair is assessed very accurately and the automatic timing is not used carelessly, results can be as good as those achieved with the manual method. The risks of over-treatment, with associated skin damage, and under-treatment, with high regrowth problems, are obvious, if a 'blanket' use of identical current intensities and length of application are applied to widely differing hairs. The choice cannot be perfect for all the hairs, some could be over-treated, and some under-treated. These problems can be overcome with careful assessment of the hairs, and many operators prefer automatic timing, believing it provides fast, accurate work, and reduces the risks of over-treatment or operator error.

As long as the overall result is excellent — maximum destruction with minimum skin damage — the method is not important. Carelessness can occur whichever method is used, so attention to basic points of technique remains the most important element in successful work. Using the advanced frequencies available enables discomfort to be minimized, whilst improving results for the client.

4

Choice of needles

FERRIE STEEL NEEDLES

Ferrie steel needles are the most widely used and provide a durable needle in a variety of diameters to suit differing hair conditions. They are also available in a sterile disposable form, for example 'ONE-TIME' or 'STEREX' needles. Available in diameter from .003 to .006 in, the Ferrie needle stands up to sterilization well, by hot or cold methods, and is very robust within the clinic and training situation. The fine needles are mounted in a uniform shank, which means all the varied diameter needles can be used in most standard needle holders. Needles must make excellent contact in the holder, so always check that the needle you plan to buy can be used in your existing needle holder.

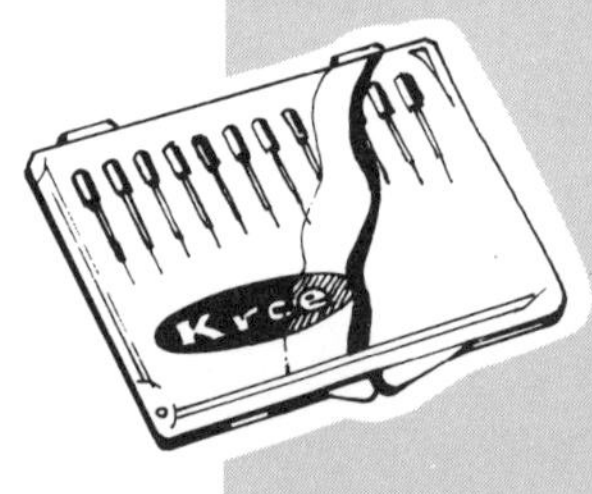

The steel used in the Ferrie needle is hardened and carries the current very uniformly and steadily, dissipating it evenly from the needle, with the main energy reacting with the skin tissues of the matrix area of the hair and the walls of the follicle at its base. Inevitably there is a discharge of destructive current into the surrounding tissues, and upwards towards the surface, but this can be minimized by good technique — holding the probe very steady, pausing fractionally after discharging the current before withdrawing the needle, and being extremely careful about the strength of current used. This almost unnoticeable pause after current discharge prevents the current from arcing back to follow the movement of the withdrawing needle, and centralizes the main destructive action of the current where needed, to destroy the follicle's capacity to regenerate another hair.

Ferrie needles stand up to continuous use very well and can be heat sterilized using a 'hot bead' type of sterilizer. With new sterilization requirements in force in the United Kingdom, the older methods of sterilization no longer provide adequate protection against bacterial and viral infections (using the machine as the source of heat sterilization, wiping needles with spirit etc.). It is also the case that most modern epilation machines can be operated on a wide range of frequencies and these frequencies do not have the power to ensure needle sterility. Alternative methods of sterilization are now required, such as the chemical vapour method or the new hot bead method which is used within the

optical field and is now available to the electrologist for her needle care. With the new licensing and registration controls coming into force in many counties of the United Kingdom, and likely to be adopted nationally, the requirements for adequate sterilization methods have increased (see Chapter 10, 'Essential Facts about Sterilization').

Remember that, like all needles, the Ferrie steel becomes blunt and needs replacement immediately if even slightly imperfect, as it cannot perform a good job. In the training situation in inexperienced hands, needles should be checked carefully under the magnifier for faults before use, to prevent the possibility of a needle fracture occurring. Consider the strain that a needle is placed under in the actual epilation process, and if in addition it has been bent, kinked or straightened, these weak areas will have become internally fractured and the passing of the current could complete the fracture causing the needle to break right off. In fact this seldom happens, which says something for the quality of Ferrie needles, and the care that goes into their manufacture, but operators often use their needles long after it would have been wise to discard them. The improvement in technique when working with a new needle makes the small cost involved seem a very worthwhile investment.

CHOICE OF NEEDLES

(a) Different hair and skin conditions need different needles for best results. Lip hair may need an insulated needle or a very fine Ferrie steel needle, .003 in diameter; chin hair could require a .004 in diameter needle, while stronger sideburn hair may need the strength of a .005 in diameter needle in severe cases

(b)–(d) Supersensitive areas, such as the eyebrows, where skin marking is a problem, may require insulated needles

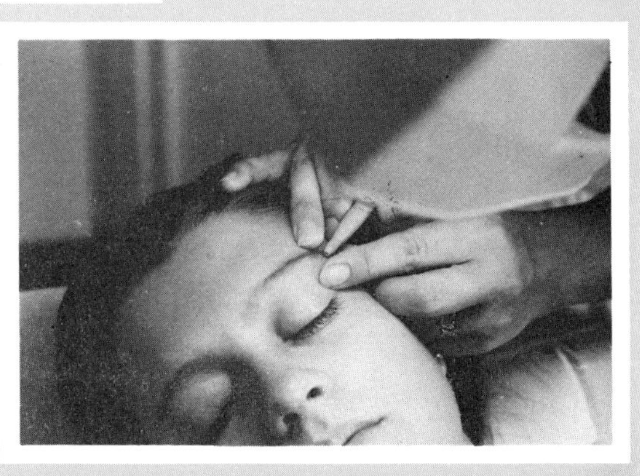

(c)

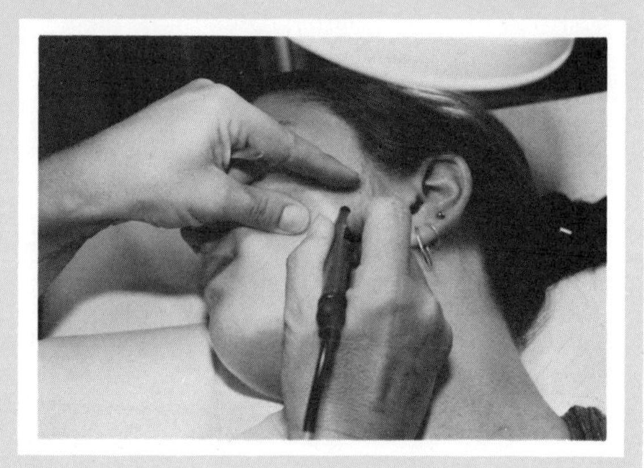

(d)

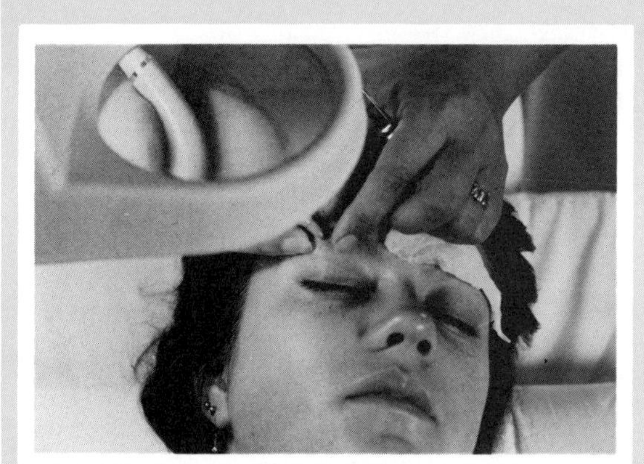

STERILIZED INDIVIDUAL NEEDLES

Sterilized Ferrie steel needles are an innovation, and will become an essential part of the treatment costing in the future in many parts of the world. As new advances are made to help the operator improve the quality of the service she offers, they should be welcomed and assessed, as that is the sign of an industry with a responsible outlook, eager to improve itself for the public good. When equipment of 20 years ago is looked at now, it seems unbelievable that it could have been used to do a professional job — and that is progress in action helping us in our work.

The needles are first packed in individual packets, and are then sterilized by gamma irradiation in batches through their clear wrappings. Their sterility is indicated by red dots on the outside of each needle packet. These dots start out yellow, and being sensitive to the gamma sterilization process, change to red as the needles are treated. Medical tools, hypodermics, sterile packs, etc., are all sterilized in this way, in quantity, and previously packed, so we are sharing some very advanced technology.

DISPOSABLE NEEDLES — STERILE

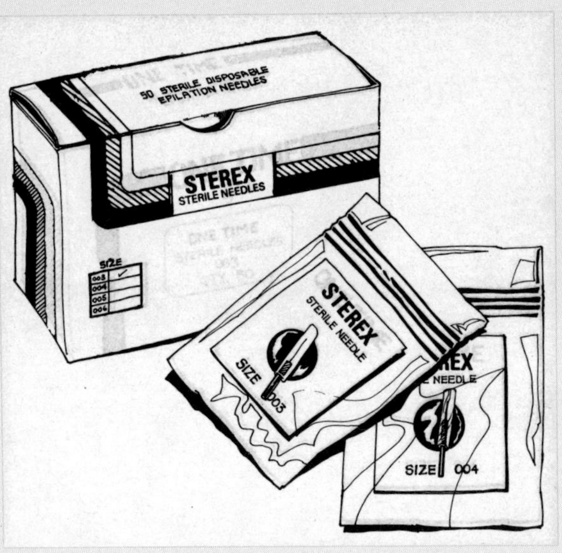

As the sterilization process is expensive, gamma sterilized needles will remain a little more costly than normal steel needles until they are used more generally. They do provide an excellent safeguard for both the operator and her client, however, and ensure treatment commences with a sterile needle in perfect condition each time. Needles are taken from the wrapping, held by the small plastic cover to avoid finger contact and inserted into the needle holder, ready for use, and discarded after one treatment. Although this does not reduce the need for normal hygienic measures to be taken within and after the actual treatment, it does provide added security from the risks of cross-infection. After the problems in recent years of the danger of passing jaundice from one person to another through infected needles (luckily no incidents of this kind have occurred within the electrology field so far), a great deal more attention has been given to the dangers of cross-infection. Certainly it is an area worth giving some serious consideration when a solution is presented, using well-known needles, but in a new sterilized form for our convenience and use. The cost of the *ONE-TIME* use sterile needle is passed directly to the customer, who knows its value because of consumer awareness created in the news media.

ROUNDED PROBE INSULATED NEEDLES

Also fairly new and proving very useful in treatment are the rounded probe insulated needles, which have special insulated material round most of the length of the needle leaving only the

probe area exposed to carry the bulk of the diathermy 'heat' current. This has obvious advantages, as the destructive force is centralized and concentrated on to the active matrix area surrounding the hair bulb. Very little current escapes to cause associated skin damage in the surrounding drier skin tissues, or can travel back up the needle towards the skin's surface affecting the walls of the follicle enclosing the hair. So the diathermy high-frequency current works best with these needles and reacts with moist tissues at the hair bulb (dermal cells, minute blood vessels, etc.) and does not affect the dry epidermal cells closer to the skin's surface so badly. Less current therefore may often be used, the skin reaction erythema (skin reddening) is reduced, the client suffers less discomfort, and healing takes place more quickly, speeding up the overall results.

Adapting to the new way of working with an insulated needle can take a little time, but may be well worth the trouble, especially for hyper-sensitive clients, those with a tendency to form skin hyper-pigmentation from heat reactions (dark marking on the skin), or for those who react badly and form dehydration pitting on the surface. Slow-healing clients can also be dealt with more successfully, as with less associated skin healing to take place the skin suffers less trauma, and being subjected to less strain, heals rapidly and is able to be treated more frequently than normal.

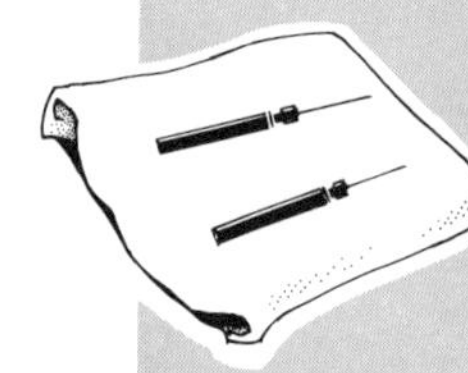

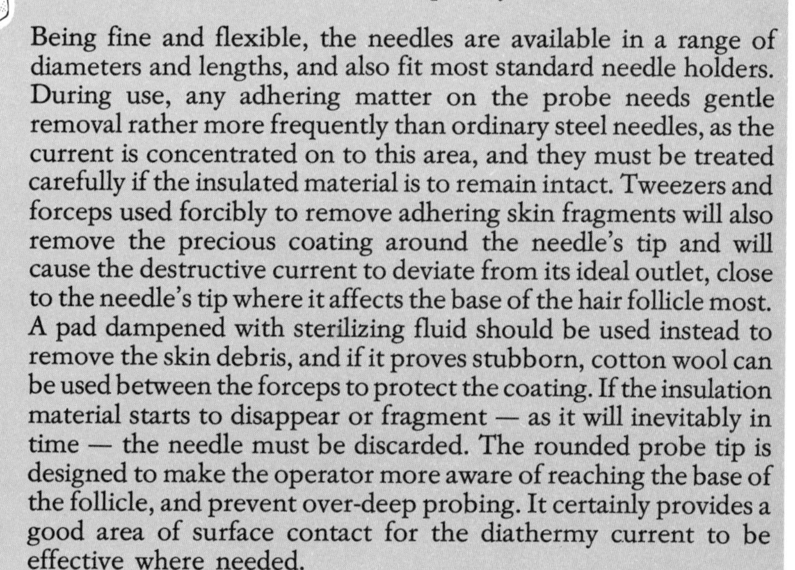

Being fine and flexible, the needles are available in a range of diameters and lengths, and also fit most standard needle holders. During use, any adhering matter on the probe needs gentle removal rather more frequently than ordinary steel needles, as the current is concentrated on to this area, and they must be treated carefully if the insulated material is to remain intact. Tweezers and forceps used forcibly to remove adhering skin fragments will also remove the precious coating around the needle's tip and will cause the destructive current to deviate from its ideal outlet, close to the needle's tip where it affects the base of the hair follicle most. A pad dampened with sterilizing fluid should be used instead to remove the skin debris, and if it proves stubborn, cotton wool can be used between the forceps to protect the coating. If the insulation material starts to disappear or fragment — as it will inevitably in time — the needle must be discarded. The rounded probe tip is designed to make the operator more aware of reaching the base of the follicle, and prevent over-deep probing. It certainly provides a good area of surface contact for the diathermy current to be effective where needed.

Operators simply have to adopt a few changes in technique to get the benefit these needles offer. They are flexible, and require that the operator take a little more care with her probe angles to achieve a good follicle entry — not a bad thing in any event.

FUTURE CHOICES

Treatments will in the future have to be costed to include the price of the disposable needle; this may happen because of a medical ruling, or simply be introduced by the industry itself (developing perhaps from a wish for a more secure means of ensuring needle sterility to eliminate the risks of cross-infection). If sterile disposable needles become the rule, their price and availability will naturally alter, and it could be a very positive step for the industry overall. The entire beauty industry is moving more and more towards disposable methods and treatments, for example, waxing by cool methods, and looking for ways to cut down on maintenance, preparation, etc., using disposable wads, paper tissues, disposable liners, etc. So it is a trend that may spread naturally to electrology, where it will have real benefits in client care as well as convenience.

Needle choice really depends on what task the needle has to perform in the destructive process. More important is the actual blend of currents the needle is carrying, and with the latest epilation machines quite a breakthrough has been achieved to reduce pain, while maintaining destructive capacity. The needles enhance this effect, and epilation is no longer the painful task it used to be. Nor does it carry the same risks of scarring for the client. Developments in needles, the needle holders, and the epilation units themselves now provide trained electrologists with equipment to match their skills.

Most important overall is the way the operator uses the needle she chooses, and her judgement on current strength, needle size, probing depth, angle, and the lightness, control and steadiness of the actual application are all part of this attention to technique. Ultimately the skill lies with the electrologist. The tools are only as good as the person who uses them.

NEEDLE CARE — A FEW POINTERS

(1) Protect your needles. A cap to fit your needle holder is essential. If your needle holder came without one, improvise. Find a pen top, or a top from a felt tip or drawing pen. A short piece of plastic tube is also ideal, just push it on every time you pause during treatment, to prevent accidental damage.

(2) Treat your needles gently and know when to throw them away; a blunt needle slows your work. *Or, if available in your country, make the change to disposable, sterile needles.*

(3) Keep needles in a safe place, sorted into sizes, ideally stored in the packaging boxes they came in. Do not allow them to get mixed up.

(4) Take care in cleaning; wipe needles with cotton wool moistened with Zephiran Chloride (or Cetavlon), held between tweezers. Clean the needles carefully before sterilization procedures.

(5) Clean the shank of the needle (in a two-piece needle — the solid base piece) to ensure a good electrical connection. If needles are not plated, and could corrode, make sure they are polished and bright, to ensure good conductivity between the holder and needle.

(6) Heat sterilize carefully (hot bead method), do not over-treat, ensure the small chamber is empty before inserting the needle, and watch the process to ensure over-heating does not occur.

(7) If needles need to be straightened, but are otherwise perfect, straighten gently between the thumb and finger, or between cotton-wool pieces. Avoid using forceps/tweezers fiercely on your needles; they can cause roughening of the shaft, making follicle entry more difficult. They can also weaken the needle, thereby reducing its life.

(8) Inspect your needles very carefully and frequently to see if the point is perfect, and to see if the coating (if present) is intact and not becoming frayed and fragmented. Discard a needle if it shows signs of stress or has been straightened many times.

(9) Keep needles in their packaging, until needed — that way they start work in a perfect state. Sterilized needles must show their gamma sterilized marking of red dots, to show that they are still sterile.

(10) Do not expect needles to go through hot bead sterilization without a certain amount of damage — accept a shorter life for your needles, *or change to using disposable sterile needles in your clinic instead.*

(11) Insulated needles gather a greater amount of skin debris, etc., on the tip of the needle, because of the concentration of current on this area. Clean the debris off gently using a cotton-wool wad soaked in Zephiran Chloride mixture (1:750 sterile water and Zephiran Chloride concentrate or Cetavlon solution — normally obtained ready mixed). Use a twisting motion to remove oily matter, etc., and prevent it getting baked on to the needle which in turn would prevent a good insertion and reduce the current effects on the hair root.

(12) Do not attempt to straighten an insulated needle with tweezers, as it will remove the coating and make the needle unusable.

(13) Choose good, fine, flexible, precision-made needles with plated shanks; use them carefully, and do not expect them to last forever.

5

Epilation faults and their remedy

Worries over the pain of epilation treatment and risks of scarring have prevented many people in the past from seeking help with their unwanted hair problem. Now with the reduced pain and reaction of the *Beauty Gallery* epilation system combined with good techniques from the operator, treatment results are dramatically improved. Taking care to avoid some of the common faults will improve technique even further.

EXCESSIVE REGROWTH

Excessive regrowth — unless from hormone influences — is nearly always related to inaccurate techniques, such as probing faults and/or not getting the current to the right area where it can be effective. Use of insufficient current intensity can also be a reason for hair returning more than would be considered normal. This may be because the client's pain threshold is low, or the skin itself acts as a limitation to the amount of current that can be used. Poor skin healing, hypersensitivity, tendencies to heat reactions, severe reactions, etc., all point to a need for current restrictions if the skin is not to be damaged by the epilation process. The advantages of an epilation system where *skin reaction is reduced, while results are maintained,* is evident.

Regrowth may also be a result of too little current reaching the active matrix area of the hair root due to hand movement when connecting the current. This causes needle movement and spillage of current into the surrounding tissues, with severe skin reaction in the area of the follicle. The correct intensity of current is chosen and applied, but because of poor hand control the effect of the current on the follicle is minimal. If the hair follicle's capacity to regenerate a new hair has not been destroyed by accurate work, even though the present hair may have been removed, a new hair will regrow exactly as it was previously, not weakened in any way by the strength of the epilation application.

PROBING FAULTS

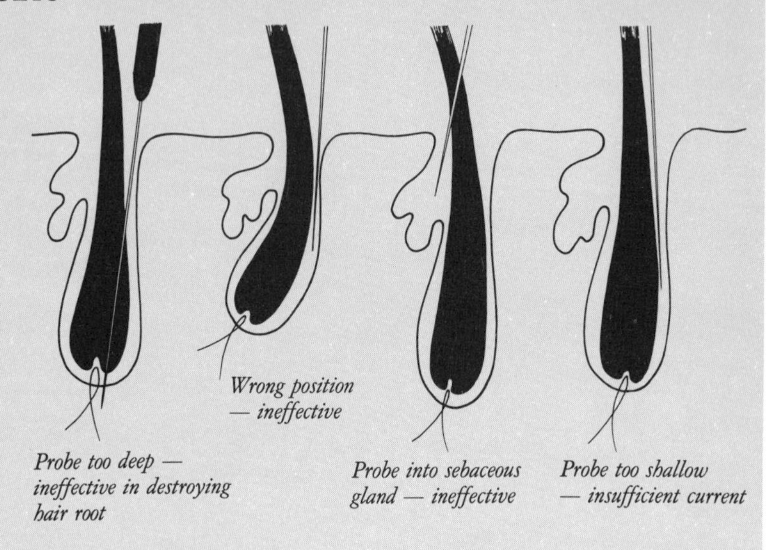

If the current has been discharged in the wrong place — too deep, too shallow, wrong angle, etc. — then the hair follicle's ability to regenerate a new hair will remain intact, and regrowth will be excessive. For this reason, when working correctly, speed is not always as important as accuracy. (For further information on probing faults see *Principles and Techniques for the Electrologist,* by Ann Gallant.)

DEHYDRATION/OPEN PORES/POOR SKIN TEXTURE

Dehydration and loss of texture is a result of too much current which causes skin damage, trauma (shock to the skin), which when it heals, contracts causing the skin to become dry and pits to form. These pits can take on the appearance of small punch-like marks in the skin, which are very obvious and unattractive. Severe pitting is usually a result of healing after surface burns have been caused by excessive use of current too close to the surface, causing 'white ringing' or burns. It can also be due to the current being discharged too deep into the skin, past the base of the follicle. An excessive amount of current, discharged in error to compensate for inaccuracy, can damage the skin germinal layer, and cause changes in actual skin formation leaving dips on the skin's surface.

PERMANENT PITTING AND SCARRING OF THE SKIN

Permanent pitting and scarring of the skin is the result of severe skin damage. The skin heals in an indented form due to damage caused to its basal layer. This damage causes the skin cells to grow permanently distorted upwards towards the surface, and scars form in a pock-like appearance. The collagen fibres of the skin's dermal layer are damaged, and the skin grows according to this indented pattern from then on. Very little can be done about skin pitting and marking when established, they must just be avoided, but it is important to record their presence on a new client's record card at the start of treatment, so that the operator cannot be blamed for any previous damage. The situation can be tactfully discussed with the client to gain her co-operation with the treatment plan and home-care routines proposed, to avoid a repetition of the problem occurring.

WHITE RINGING/BURNS

White ringing around a follicle during treatment can result in a loss of pigment, leaving white spots known as *hypopigmentation,* or dark marking known as *hyperpigmentation.* The burn reaction which causes the white ringing, swelling, oedema (fluid and swelling), relates to excessive use of current too close to the skin's surface, or hand movement while the current is being discharged. It can also be due to moving the needle while the current is flowing, for example, withdrawing the needle from the follicle

CAUSES OF WHITE RINGING

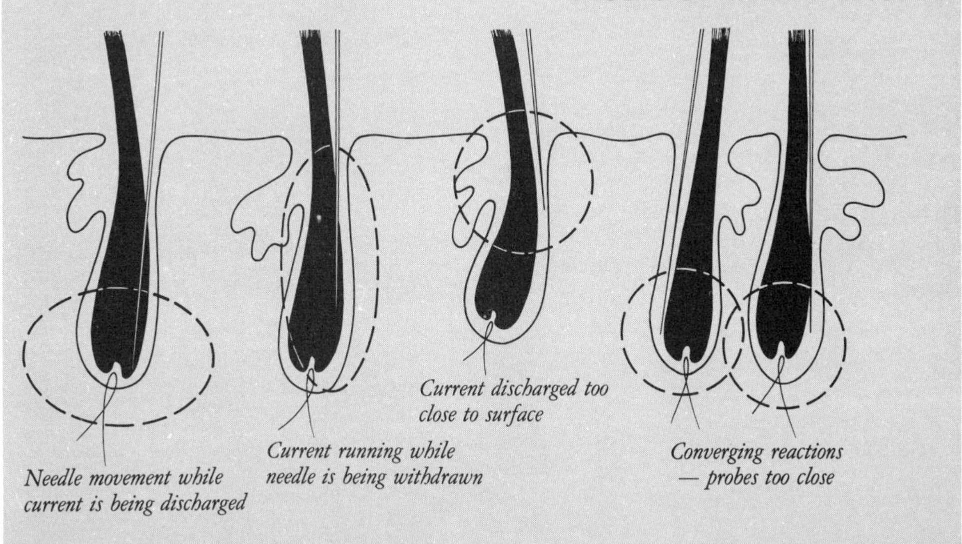

while the current is still connected, which causes the follicle walls and mouth of the follicle to be burnt and react accordingly. A normal burn reaction occurs on the skin's dry surface tissues; they become raised, white and blanched, and afterwards turn red, angry and sore, and can form normal burn-scars. As a result of the injury and shock to the tissues, the skin can sometimes heal in an indented form, or become raised and cyst-like in the area, depending on the individual's healing capacity and skin type.

Lack of steadiness of hands in the early stages of learning epilation can result in a tremendous amount of white ringing and skin reactions; these are simple heat reactions in the tissues due to spillage of the short wave diathermy current. Instead of the current finding its moist, soft, hair root 'goal' at the base of the follicle, it reacts against dry horny skin tissues causing a straightforward burn. White ringing can be prevented by making sure the probe is accurate, deep enough, and the current is not allowed to keep running when the needle is being removed from the follicle. A momentary 'pause' after the discharge of the current, while the needle is still in the follicle, correctly placed, will prevent this happening. Most of the unsteadiness of the hands which causes the spillage of current to occur comes as a direct result of lack of confidence with the needle holder, needle and use of forceps (tweezers). By continual practice on the leg and body hairs until these tools feel at home in the hand, the operator will overcome poor control of her small tools, and can then concentrate on her probing techniques exclusively. (For further information about building up technique in epilation, see *Principles and Techniques for the Electrologist,* by Ann Gallant.)

PIGMENTATION PROBLEMS

Skin can become darker or lighter after application of the short wave diathermy current. Although this problem is reduced with the *Beauty Gallery* epilation system, which has been designed to reduce the heat effects in the tissue, it is still a factor of epilation treatment, and can be avoided by good technique.

Hyperpigmentation (dark patches) occurs as a result of heat reaction in the skin which activates the pigment molecules in the area, causing them to rise to the surface and become apparent. This is a special problem with dark-skinned or sometimes pale-skinned but dark-haired clients, where freckle-like spots appear after the initial period following treatment. Use of insulated steel needles helps the problem, also working with a slightly lower intensity of current for fractionally longer application times. Pigmentation requires an adjustment in technique, and is really not a fault as such, but rather something that occurs but can be prevented if it is noticed.

Hypopigmentation (white areas with a total loss of colour) can also result from skin damage caused by the current. The pigment molecules lose their capacity to function, and the client ends up with white glassy-looking patches on the skin, which are just as unsightly as the dark marking.

Both pigmentation problems require careful work and attention to technique to avoid their recurrence. Initial inspection of the face within the consultation period may provide a clue to the client's tendency to the problem, either from previous epilation treatment or from a natural inclination to forming dark pigmentation patches from sun exposure.

Spacing the probes carefully, working with the minimum current possible, using special insulated needles, taking extra trouble over after-care, and cooling down the skin throughout the application with special soothing lotions will all help where pigmentation seems to present a problem.

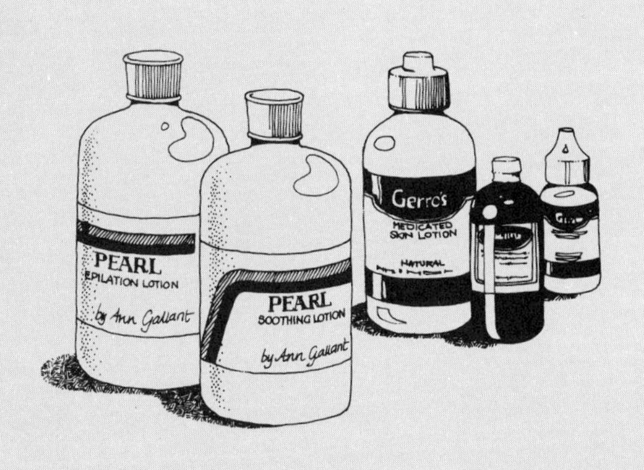

6

Organizing the epilation treatment

Making a treatment plan that the client can cope with is an important aspect of overall success. A way has to be found to make it possible for the client to carry on a normal life while she is undergoing removal of her superfluous or unwanted hair. If the problem is not severe, it may be possible for her to leave the hair growth intact for the operator to reduce progressively with each treatment. Many clients have lived with the problem so long that any slight improvement in appearance is welcomed and seen as a step forward. Others expect 'instant results' and must be tactfully told that this is impossible with epilation because of the limitations of the skin, but that a good result can be achieved with a little patience. It should always be stressed that it is the only method that can get rid of the hairs *permanently.*

Many clients who consult an electrologist, however, have a noticeable hair problem on the upper-lip and chin, which they remove by temporary methods, and are not prepared to leave obvious for the world to know about. So a way has to be found for them to maintain a groomed appearance while the treatment is progressing. This may mean working on certain areas of the skin at a time, working after weekends to allow a small amount of growth to be present, or treating the client in the evening after her day's work. Even clients with a severe problem can usually disguise the hairs with an opaque make-up base which stops the stubble showing through.

The most successful way to treat the skin area where the hairs are positioned is to space the probes over the entire area, lip and chin if both are involved, so that no probes converge in their heat reactions against each other. The distance between probes should be ideally $\frac{1}{8}$ to $\frac{1}{10}$ cm (approximately $\frac{1}{16}$ in), and the time between repeat treatments on the same area approximately 14 days. This allows for skin healing to take place, and in cases of extreme sensitivity or poor healing longer periods may need to elapse

between treatments. Clients with allergy-prone skins or who suffer from diabetes mellitus may need the probe spacing and the treatment intervals extended to help them cope with treatment.

If the hair problem is extensive and the client needs to be encouraged to persist in her epilation efforts, then areas of the face, throat, etc., can be treated in rotation (lip one week, chin another), to move progress forward and prevent the client from becoming despondent. Then only the client's time and finances will limit progress, and she should be encouraged to put in as much effort as possible into solving her problem, especially until a turning point is reached where she can see a real improvement in her hair problem. Working in rotation requires that very accurate treatment records are kept to show which areas have been worked on; the skin may appear healed but might have deep healing still to take place in the skin's lower stratum, and if the area is worked on again prematurely, a bad reaction could occur.

CLIENT CO-OPERATION

If the client is unable to leave her unwanted hairs to grow between treatments, she must be advised to remove them by some method which does not distort the hair growth, for example she could cut them or use a depilatory cream to remove them from the surface. Plucking and waxing should not be used while epilation treatment is in progress, and if the skin is very sensitive neither should depilatory creams be used, as the skin can itself become sensitized by the use of the chemical hair dissolvent. Hair and skin are essentially rather similar in structure, so as the hairs are dissolved using depilatory creams the skin also becomes physically thinner and more inclined to reactions, which is not helpful to the epilation treatment and slows progress.

Clients with a major problem, often thought of as needing *remedial epilation work* even though they do not make up a major proportion of clinic clients, require a slightly different approach in treatment. The main reason for this is due to the strength of the hairs, and their hormone influenced origins. These clients can be allowed to continue cutting the hairs or even shaving if that is what they are used to and their problem is severe and widespread. Plucking, waxing, etc., should be discouraged, as not only does it prevent the hairs being available for treatment, and makes them difficult to probe and grasp afterwards with forceps, it can also cause follicle disruption and distortion. This makes these already difficult hairs even more awkward to probe successfully and slows progress for the client.

Clients who have previously not removed their superfluous hairs in any other way apart from cutting them off from the surface, shaving, using depilatory creams, etc., will be found to have much

less regrowth than those who have plucked, tweezed, waxed, etc., for some time prior to seeking professional help for their problem.

The treatment can be organized so that one area is treated at a time, for example, the lip, or side chin, jawline, etc., to allow the client to maintain a groomed appearance leaving this small area only available for the actual epilation application. This does mean that the work becomes concentrated in this area and so additional care must be taken over pre-care and after-care measures, and all means available must be used to minimize skin reaction, swelling, erythema (skin reddening), etc. Use of insulated needles helps as does the use of ozone vapour steaming before and after the application to reduce reaction and promote skin healing, while minimizing the risks of skin infection. Client co-operation over home-care measures is vital in order to avoid a poor result; carelessness over skin hygiene at home can make or break the overall success of the treatment.

HOME-CARE MEASURES

If the client is prepared to give the electrologist her full co-operation by regular attendances and by caring for her skin at home to keep it in good condition, she will achieve an excellent result in the minimum time possible. If home hygiene is poor, however, and the skin becomes infected after treatment through client carelessness, progress will be slow. So operators must not provide any opportunity for the client to be lax in her home-care support measures, but must provide all she needs, and advise her exactly how to help the skin to heal well. If kept clean during treatment and soothed throughout with special lotions, the skin is really very good at healing itself. Once the skin has formed a barrier within the follicle to surface dust, etc., then infection risks are very slight. It is this period immediately after treatment when the skin is irritated slightly, and the follicles are open and rather susceptible to transient bacteria entering them and causing problems, that great care must be taken over skin hygiene and skin protection. If the skin has been kept cool and settled throughout the application, reaction is minimized and less risk of inflammation and swelling occurring from the diathermy heat is present. Padding the skin immediately the work is completed reduces discomfort and swelling in the tissues, and reduces the need for complicated home-care measures. If a reaction has not been caused, there is unlikely to be any skin irritation. The *Beauty Gallery* epilation system works on this principle, avoiding unwanted reaction associated with pain and heat, while maintaining hair destruction.

Basic home-care measures to look after the skin include immediate protection with a medicated powder, soothing lotion or calming

cream, to close the area to bacteria which could enter the hair follicles, and a gentle approach to dealing with the skin for the next few days after treatment. The powder or soothing lotion should be the only product put on the skin during the first 24 hours, as the area is already clean and can be worked around when washing or cosmetically cleansing the rest of the face. After this period, the powder or soothing lotion can be reapplied after gentle washing or cleansing, and if make-up is then to be worn, it can be applied over this protection. Many of the creams used for after-care are based on calamine or azulene, both well-known calmers and healers, though some people do get a reaction to azulene so this should be checked with the client. Medicated lotions are not really needed to heal the skin, and can act as an irritant in their action, but in cases where the skin has developed an infection in the follicles, due to carelessness or poor health factors, then a very diluted solution of Savlon or Cetavlon can be used to wipe over the skin. Both lotions have as their active ingredient a known anti-inflammatory and healing agent which calms and settles the skin and promotes healing.

Many electrologists rely on well-known soothing formulae from major cosmetic houses so that they have an attractive product to sell to the client, one that she will not mind having on her cosmetic shelf. Others prefer simple natural formulae, based on herbal elements to reduce inflammation and promote healing in a more gentle way. The most important thing overall is to do the work well, use a good machine, and take care to prevent infection occurring by maintaining a high standard of hygiene in the clinic and give advice to the client about how she should care for her skin at home.

INVOLVING THE CLIENT IN HER PROGRESS

If the client works with the electrologist to achieve the desired results, she will feel involved in her progress and will not get so despondent when hairs do not disappear as fast as she wished. Having sufficient hair available to be epilated within the treatment sessions is also sensible, and helps the operator to work well and achieve the maximum result for the client in the short treatment time of 15 to 20 minutes normally involved. If clients have been plucking or waxing their hairs prior to epilation treatment, they have to be encouraged to let the hairs grow in order that they can be dealt with. Clients must come for treatment with sufficient hairs apparent so that the hairs can be accurately probed with regard to their angle as they leave the skin. Excessively short hairs — just removed by creams or shaving — are not only difficult and slow to treat and hard to get hold of, but also provide little guidance as to the probe angle required for accuracy. The client

gets a slower treatment and less satisfactory results, so this is one area where a bit of tactful conversation to improve client co-operation is necessary for overall success.

TREATMENT CONSULTATION

It is important to explain some basic points about epilation to the client on the initial consultation, to help her understand and co-operate with the treatment. If the initial inquiry has been made by telephone, an information brochure describing the service may be sent which stresses the qualifications of the operator, and details the procedures involved. This saves a lot of precious time for the busy practitioner, and saves dealing with time wasters. Often, however, it is necessary to see the client's condition first hand in order to be able to advise her on treatment details, and this is completed on an initial consultation visit. All these points can be combined into a short introductory treatment to demonstrate to the client that the application is quite bearable, and gets her started while her interest and courage are present. This initial visit sets the tone for the entire professional relationship, and it is here the operator either gains or loses herself a new client — so it is worth giving it some thought.

Information gained at this initial consultation will end up on the client's record card as the starting point for the treatment — but first the client has to be won, and this can be achieved in many ways. The client has to feel confident she is in good hands, that her problem can be solved without undue pain, distress or embarrassment. The operator must, therefore, be positive and inspire confidence by her manner, her clinic's appearance and equipment, and she should give evidence of her diploma qualifications. Factors such as the length of treatment required, cost of sessions, and how epilation works to achieve its permanent results should all be discussed briefly, but openly, so that the client feels informed and in caring, trained hands.

If the consultation proceeds into a short epilation treatment session — which makes good business sense — careful details can then be taken to ensure the individual is suitable for treatment and that there are no contra-indications or reasons why the treatment should not be given.

CLIENT'S RECORD CARD

The record card should record the client's personal details, such as her name, initials, address and telephone numbers (home and work), her doctor's name and number and own brief medical history. This will have special reference to any gynaecological history, pregnancies, number of children, their ages, hysterectomy, menopause, hormone replacement therapy (HRT) or use of the contraceptive pill. Whether the client has had previous epilation

TREATMENT DATE, DURATION, AND DETAILS OF PAYMENT

An accurate record should be kept to provide a secondary check against the appointment book of how much treatment has been actually undertaken in terms of hours and cost. This is useful, both for the client who may feel her treatment is rather a slow process, and for the operator, to check her income, especially if working on commission for an employer or within a chain of electrology clinics where earnings are based on takings.

SKIN REACTION TO TREATMENT

Any adverse reaction can be recorded and may guide or alter the epilation application in the future. Any reactions related by the client which occurred several days after the treatment can also be put down on the next treatment's details. Heat reactions, dark freckles at the mouths of the follicles, soreness in the area, infection, etc., may all indicate that changes in the technique could be useful. Use of different needles, power intensity, spacing of probes, more time between appointments, different home-care measures may all need consideration. It is only by watching results and gauging skin reactions that the operator knows she is achieving good progress for her clients.

7

The working position — equipment for the job

Where the operator works and the equipment she chooses are vital points in business success and a happy professional life. A light attractive environment is pleasant for both client and operator, and as it can make so much difference to working comfort and good technique, it is worth careful consideration to get it right. The way you set yourself up initially may help you earn your

THE IMPORTANCE OF THE EQUIPMENT

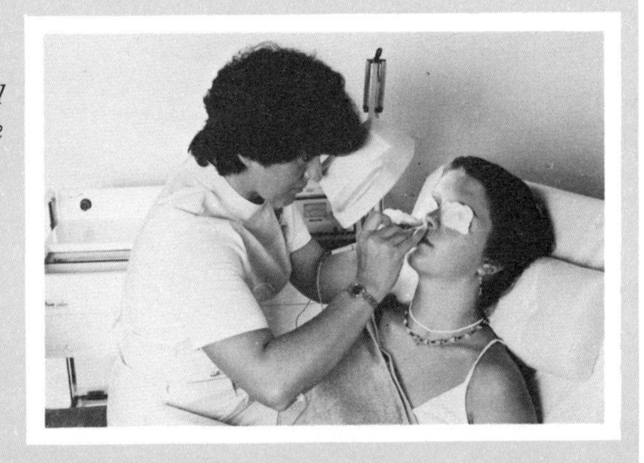

(a) Equipment should be close to hand and the operator should be able to work comfortably

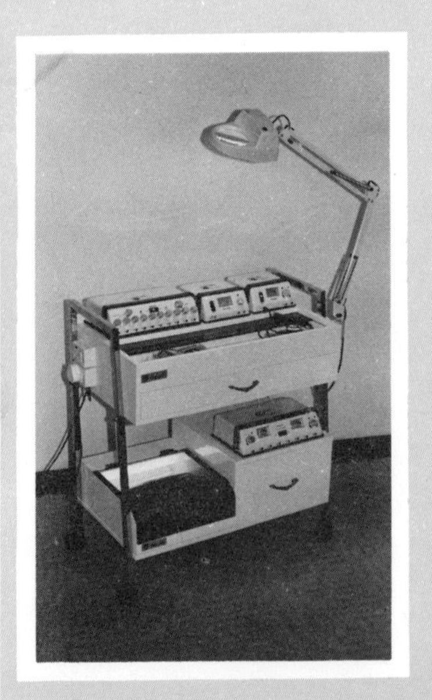

(b) The Beauty Gallery *system provides everything needed: epilation unit, space for tools, magnifier, sterilizer, safe storage for small equipment — such as forceps and lotions*

living in your chosen field for the rest of your working life, so you should feel at home with the equipment you use and be able to rely on it to do its job well.

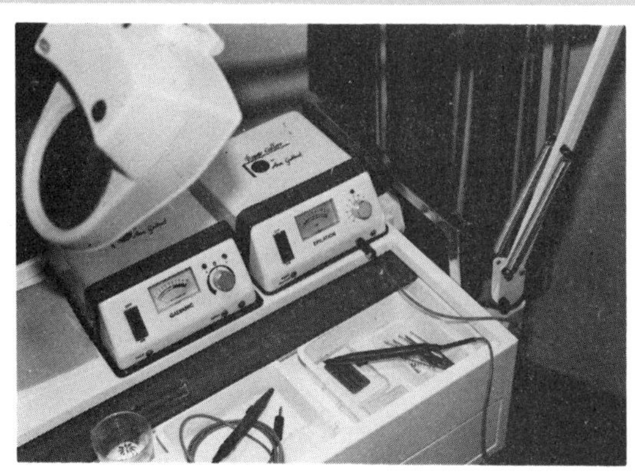

(c) The epilation unit, the magnifier and the sterilizer can be used independently from the Beauty Gallery *system*

A comfortable treatment couch is a must, ideally multi-positional to enable all areas of the client to be treated easily. An adjustable stool is also required, plus an illuminated magnifier, an epilation unit, a sterilizer, and some provision for storage of small tools (forceps, needle holders, needles, etc.). A system such as the *Beauty Gallery* is a compact and attractive working unit, designed for the operator's needs. It provides the basis for the best of techniques to be applied, and a sound business to be developed. If the operator is also a qualified therapist, she can move swiftly from therapy to electrology treatments without disruption to the client. This increases the operator's earning capacity and efficiency quite dramatically.

The operator must be comfortable in her working position, her posture should always be correct to avoid back strain, and she should be able to reach and work on her client with control. She should also be in control of her epilation unit and able to make minute adjustments to the current intensity as needed. She must have the client well-positioned for accurate probing of the hairs, and have her small tools close to hand, either in a sterilizer storage, or in a small drawer to keep them safe and clean. If the operator works at getting herself comfortable, then steadiness of the hands, control of the needle holder and forceps will present no problem. If she is uncomfortable, however, she will suffer from back ache, strained arms, etc., perhaps due to the stool being too high or low, or the client being in the wrong position, too far away, head too low or high; in this case the probes will be difficult, and accurate work will not be achieved. Both operator and client will suffer — so it is only fair to sort out the working position before starting work. Get to know the positions the couch can offer, and use its flexible positioning if you have it available. Do not be afraid to

put your client where you want her, clients do not mind, they like to feel cared for and skilfully placed in the best position. It reflects your professional expertise if you show with confidence that you know what you are doing. Tucking a client in tight against you while working on her also provides you with instant feedback to what she is feeling, and tells you when she has had enough treatment, even if her appointment time is not over.

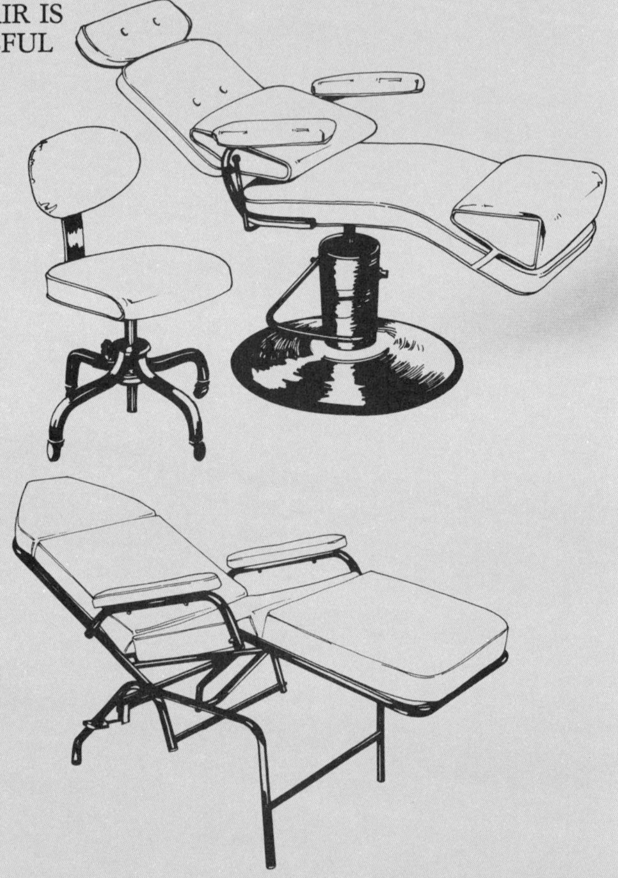

A WELL-DESIGNED CHAIR IS A MUST FOR A SUCCESSFUL PRACTICE

The small tools needed include the needle holder, or ideally two to allow for swift change-overs from one needle diameter to another when working on varied hair growth. The new switch control holders allow very fast and efficient work as the current is switched off instantly as the finger releases the switch with a tiny 'click', allowing no flow of current to occur after the current is discharged. If the needle holder is a plain type, used with a foot switch, it operates in an identical way except that it is the foot that triggers the switch inside the machine which turns the chosen current on or off.

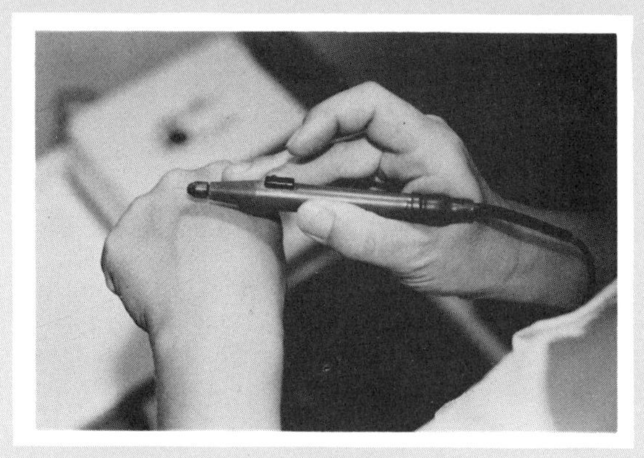

EPILATION EQUIPMENT AND SMALL TOOLS

(a) The new switch control needle holder connects the current electronically to avoid errors

(b) A selection of forecps is essential

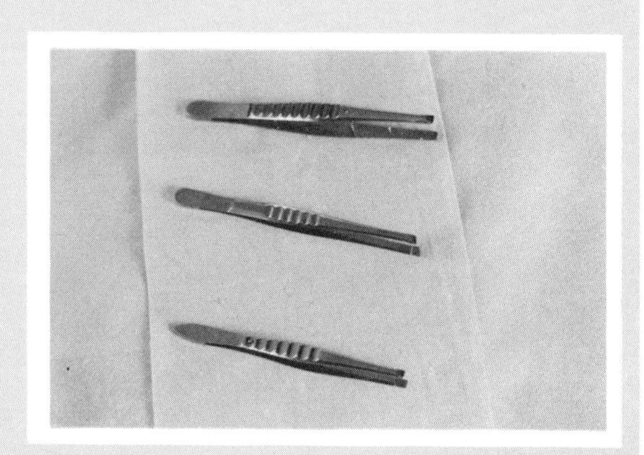

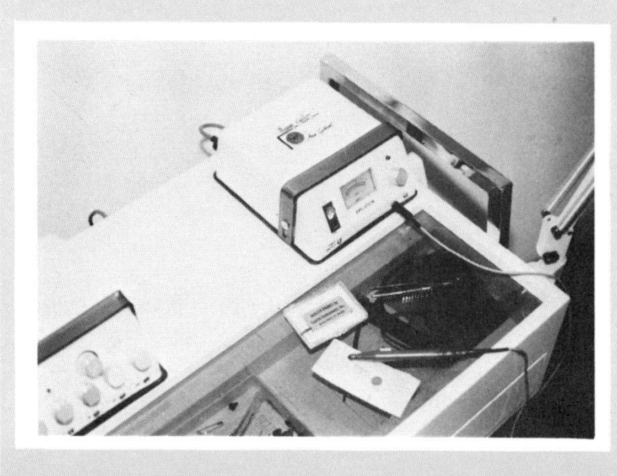

(c) A selection of needles for all hair types is needed. Spare needle holders are available with this epilation system to allow for swift needle changeovers

A selection of needles is needed, plus forceps (tweezers), cotton wool in a closed container, a waste bin, and a method of sterilizing the tools and needles are essential. If sterilization is not incorporated into the treatment system being used, it can be provided separately — by bacteria/vapour methods (as with the *Beauty Gallery* sterilizer), or using ultraviolet rays, in a cabinet, or cold water sterilization methods, making sure rust inhibiting sterilization fluids are used otherwise your tools will rust in the water bath. Needles can be sterilized by using the small 'hot bead' method which safely provides a sterile needle in seconds. If available, sterile, disposable needles may be used, and these are rapidly becoming the most popular and convenient choice for the busy operator. Disposable needles like 'ONE-TIME' or 'STEREX' eliminate all possibility of human error spoiling the sterility of the needle used.

HOT BEAD STERILIZER

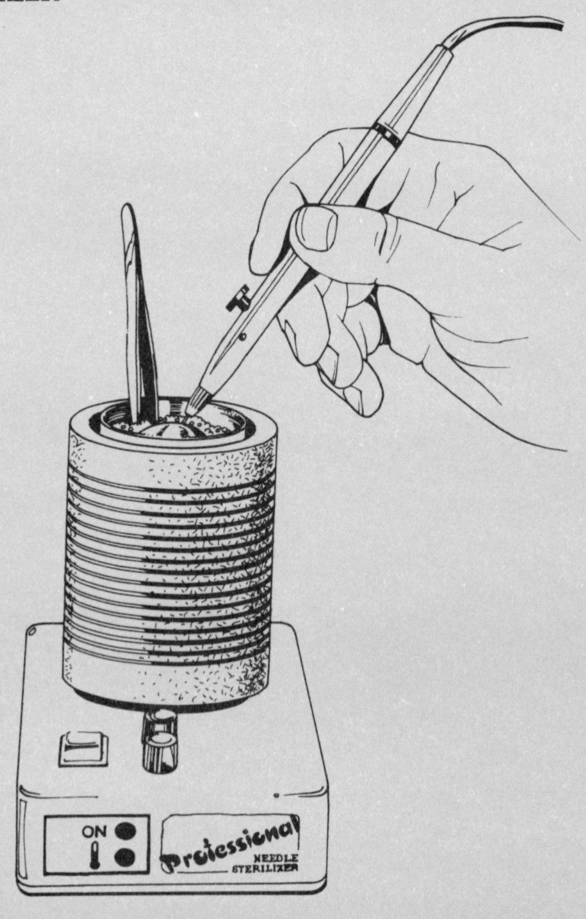

Needles sterilized by vapour methods simply need placing in the trays provided in the sterilizer after cleaning, drying and wrapping in gauze to avoid losing them. The *Beauty Gallery* sterilizer is very simple and effective, and only requires a small amount of sterilizing fluid to be dropped on a sponge insert in the back plastic tray of the sterilizer. The heat of the illuminated lamp in the cabinet vaporizes the fluid and in 20 minutes everything in the cabinet is sterile if it was clean when it went in. The tools can remain in the sterilizer until needed, with it switched off, keeping them in a sterile atmosphere. When needed they can be lifted out in the tray provided and placed in the shallow trough on the top level of the *Beauty Gallery,* still in the tray as this avoids damage to these costly and fragile tools. The sterilizer fluid only needs topping up if the sponge becomes dry, and should not be over-pungent when the unit's perspex lid is raised as this indicates too much fluid has been used. A few drops daily in a warm atmosphere is all that is needed; in cooler climates, every other day is quite adequate. The sterilizer should not be left on, but used to do its job and then switched off and then used as a sterile storage cupboard.

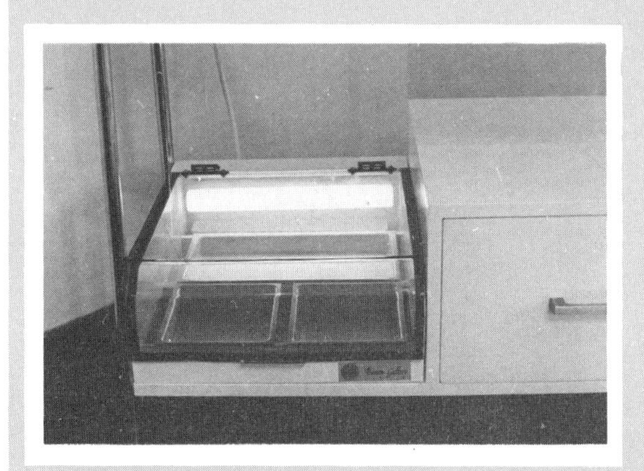

THE STERILIZER PROVIDES HYGIENIC MEASURES TO SAFEGUARD THE CLIENT

(a)

(b)

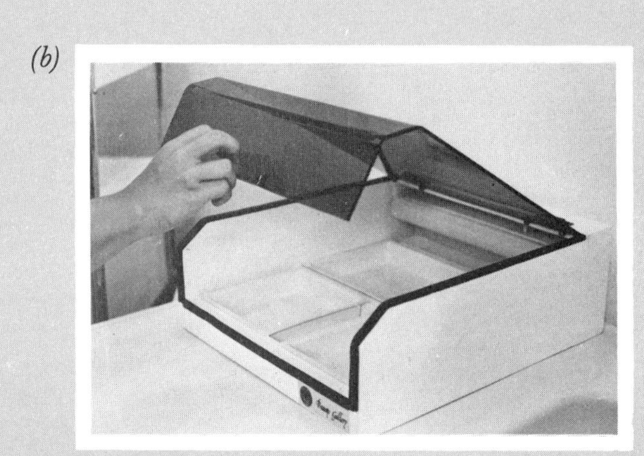

Heat sterilizing can be used to good effect during the actual epilation application, by running the forceps gently up the length of the needle, with the intensity on the epilation unit set at a moderate level of 4 to 5. This is not recommended for insulated needles as it can damage the protective coating along the main length of the needle shaft. Sterile disposable needles make this task unnecessary for needles, but a sterilizer will still be needed for the other small tools, forceps, etc., and is a natural part of achieving a hygienic environment for the client to receive treatment (see Chapter 10, 'Essential Facts about Sterilization', for regulations in force).

An illuminated magnifier provides a good substitute for natural daylight, and saves strain on the eyes, while also acting as a breath shield between the operator and the client. If magnifiers are attached to a working system like the *Beauty Gallery,* this avoids having to have a separate pedestal with feet, which saves space if work is carried out in a tiny cubicle. Free-standing magnifiers are also available for those that prefer them.

The magnifier must be positioned to bring the hairs into focus, and to highlight them if fair and difficult to see. The operator should get used to repositioning her magnifier to help her vision and clarity, and eventually the movement will become automatic — slight adjustments being made when needed to throw the hairs into relief or contrast against the skin. Being able to see exactly what you are doing improves technique dramatically and prevents eyestrain occurring. Even operators with excellent eyesight should work with a magnifier, in order to preserve their sight, for a long working lifetime of rewarding and worthwhile service.

8

Applying the epilation treatment

GETTING READY FOR TREATMENT

At the start of a working day the equipment should be checked to see it is working correctly, and the needle holder prepared for work. Then it is only necessary for the small tools and commodities needed in the treatment to be assembled, and treatment can get under way. All preparation must be completed before the client arrives, and it is best if the working position is always left ready for use. A prospective client may call in at any time, and will expect to see a tidy working cubicle, so a 'tidy as you go' approach works best, and speeds work as well.

Epilation, being such a tightly timed treatment — and expensive for the client — should be set up in such a way that not a second is wasted for either the client or operator. If all equipment and supplies are placed in the storage drawer or sterilizer of, say, the *Beauty Gallery* unit, or placed under its sliding perspex cover on the top level, then everything will be close to hand and work can commence within seconds. If a simple trolley is used with plug sockets on its backboard, then the sterilizer, epilation unit and magnifier can still all be plugged in, making a neat working unit. The trolley is also available with a drawer unit under the top surface, providing for small storage of needles, spare holders, forceps, etc.

EVERYTHING NEEDED SHOULD BE CLOSE TO HAND

PREPARING THE NEEDLE HOLDER

It will be necessary to have a selection of sterilized needles available, Ferrie, insulated, disposable, etc., to give flexibility of treatment to suit all hair and skin conditions. All the needles must fit the needle holder, and most these days do have a standardized 'shank' — a heavier base for the fine needles of different diameters — making it possible to use them with standard needle holders. So the needle's fineness and length may alter, but its basic fitting which slots into the claws of the needle holder will be the same. Some needle holders, like the *Beauty Gallery* switch control needle holder, are capable of coping with a slight variation of needles, but by their very nature and the task they have to complete, it is difficult for a holder to accommodate the whole range from very fine needles (like the long flexible German insulated needles) right through to the sturdy needles used for treatment of warts, veins, etc. The contact between the needle and the metal claws of the needle holder must be excellent, so needles must be a firm fit, with no movement, and when the needle is in place — shoulders

FITTING THE NEEDLE INTO THE NEEDLE HOLDER
(a) Ensure firm contact

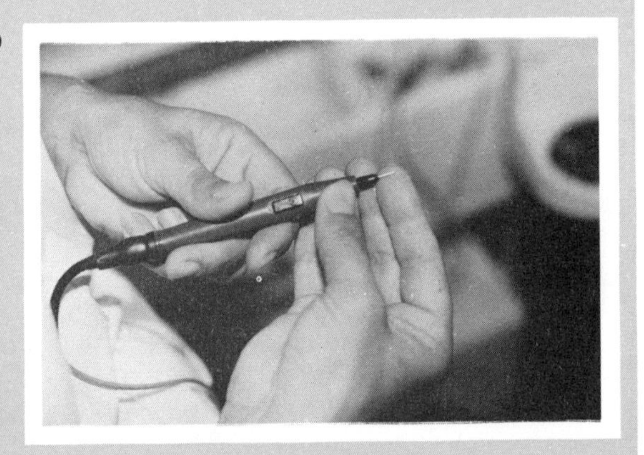

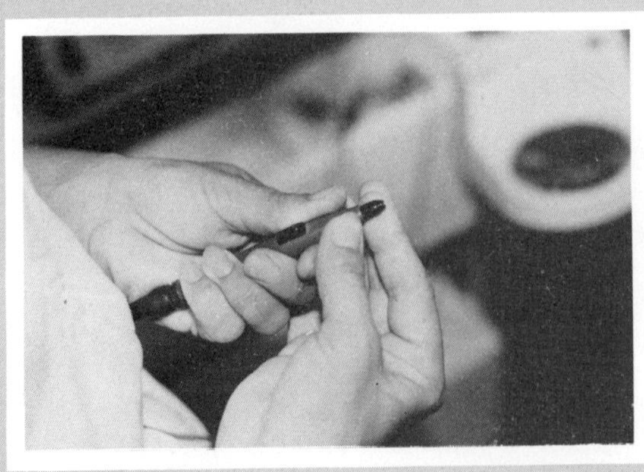

(b) Correct placing of needle in relation to claws of holder

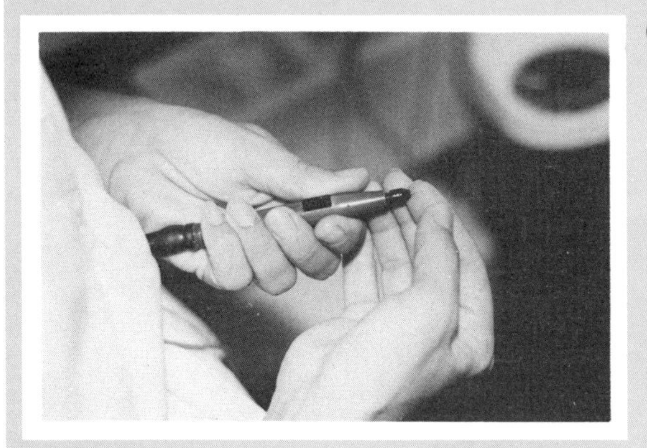

(c) Putting needle in through top of cap

showing — and the cap is tightened, there must be no looseness in the fitting. Needles should not protrude unduly, only the needle itself should show, and not much of its thicker base shank should be evident sticking out from the cap. Often it is not necessary to remove the cap entirely to change a needle — simply unscrew it a little, release the needle and remove it carefully, and replace with a different one as needed. Sterile needles such as 'ONE-TIME' and 'STEREX' are disposable and are placed direct from their wrapping into the needle holder without finger contact to spoil their sterility. When using sterile disposable needles, these are prepared just prior to use on each client, a first step in the individual client's treatment.

Once the needle holder is ready, it can be placed for safety in the shallow tray area of the *Beauty Gallery* storage system, and the perspex slide pulled over it to keep it safe until needed. A spare needle holder is always a boon when working fast or if the needle holder in use is damaged by accident. The spare one can be kept ready in the drawer, with perhaps a different diameter needle in place, then if needed it is available quickly. A small plastic length of tube can be placed right over the cap of the holder to keep the needle safe.

BASIC COMMODITIES

Basic items can be kept ready; cleansing preparations to remove make-up, soothing lotions to cool and settle the skin during treatment, and medicated creams, lotions or powders for after-care treatment. Cotton wool in a closed container, and a waste bin for soiled cotton wool, used needles, tissues, etc., is also needed. A box of tissues for protecting the client's clothes from powders, etc., and to place hairs on is also needed. A sterilizer is required, and the forceps and needles currently in use can stay in there until needed. Spares of both needles and forceps can stay in the sterilizer

cabinet just in case they are needed during treatment to replace dropped items or when replacement is indicated for other reasons. Being prepared saves delays during treatment, a valuable point when everything must run smoothly if the business is to be successful and the client to be satisifed.

PREPARATION

(a) Check the epilation unit at the start of a day's work

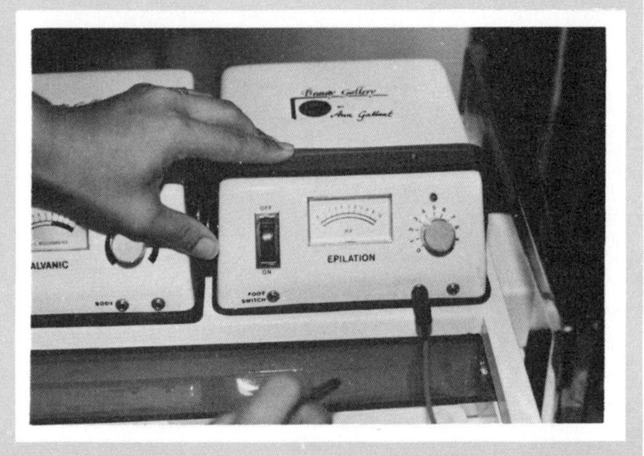

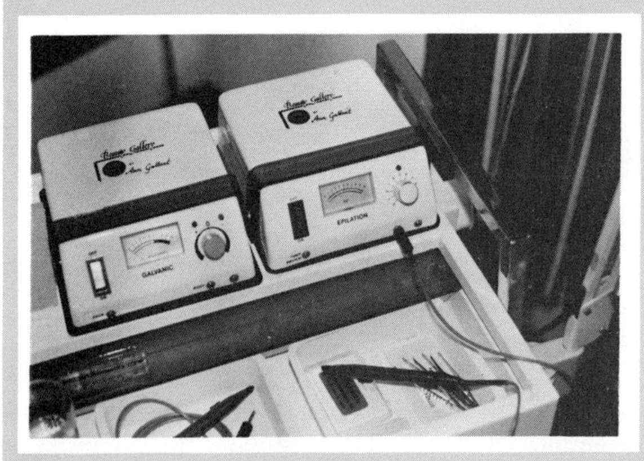

(b) Place the equipment needed in the special tray provided

(c) The power used is shown on the meter of the epilation system. This means that very accurate records can be kept

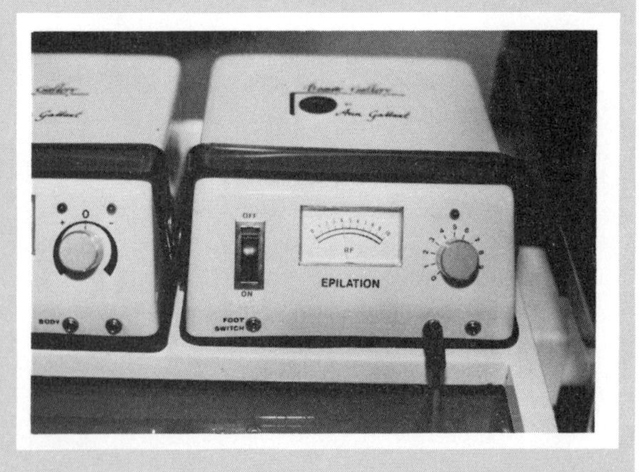

OFFERING AN EFFICIENT SERVICE

Everything that can be done to ensure a hygienic and efficient service should be done before the client's arrival — even down to having her treatment card ready to fill in or ready for reference. There is no time for running about gathering up the items needed to complete the epilation treatment once the client has arrived. The appointment time would be over before the operator was ready to do the work!

As clients may be booked every 15 to 20 minutes — even every 10 minutes in some cases — throughout the course of a day, the operator must watch her timing otherwise she will run behind with her appointments and annoy her clients. She will also find herself losing the little breaks in her working day which bring necessary physical and mental relief from this exacting work. So getting ready beforehand is one way to build up treatment efficiency, and another is to allow small breaks in the appointment bookings at odd intervals just to allow for a little overlap. Newly qualified operators, who are a little slow still, should make their appointments slightly further apart until their speed increases. In this way they can work well, not penalize the client cost-wise for the extra time, and build their own skills and confidence without pressure from outside business factors. Speed soon builds up, and after not many weeks of full-time work a pattern of technique emerges which brings the operator up to full working efficiency.

GREETING THE CLIENT

If the client is a regular one and knows the routine, she will usually come for treatment without make-up to help speed the work, and to ensure she gets maximum benefit from what is an expensive service anywhere in the world. After settling the client in the chair, the operator's hands are washed, and the client's make-up (if worn) is removed. This must be completed swiftly with gentle but effective cleansing products. Only the areas involved in treatment need be cleansed, using damp cotton-wool pieces, cotton-wool balls, or tissues. Removal of make-up must be thorough, otherwise a risk exists of introducing make-up into the follicles while they are open, exposing them to surface bacteria after the epilation treatment. This could affect healing. Removal of make-up should be effective, swift, and the skin should not be over-stimulated — for this reason a cream cleanser and damp cotton wool is very popular, as the efficiency of the product and the coolness of the dampened pieces of cotton wool avoid the need for rubbing and keep the skin settled and calm. If

the client is not wearing make-up, her skin can be simply wiped over with the soothing lotion to remove surface oils, dust, etc., so that it presents a clean, settled surface to work on. At this stage it is most important not to introduce a harsh antiseptic lotion in the mistaken belief that the skin will be 'sterilized' by it. Most antiseptics irritate the skin, causing sensory nerve reactions which make treatment more difficult. They also tend to close the pores making probing more difficult and uncomfortable for the client. Any antiseptic used on the skin must be in an extremely diluted form, so that it has no irritant properties. Ideally they should not be used in this way, but only to ensure the sterility of the items, used in close contact with the skin. The use of disposable items, tissues, head sheets, cotton wool, sterile needles etc., plus attention to good hygiene in the clinic and personal hygiene, are far more important points with which to guard against cross-infection, and impress the client in her initial judgement of the surroundings (see Chapter 10, 'Essential Facts about Sterilization').

WORKING POSITION

The clean skin is then closely inspected and the client repositioned correctly into the chair if necessary, with the area of treatment brought into the ideal position for fast work. Use of the headrest, lifting the head, or dropping it back, can all be used to help probing angles and avoid having to lean on the client. The client can be moved towards the operator or shifted up or down in the chair slightly to help overall positioning. The angle of the chair can be altered as well, plus the operator can adjust her stool up and down, or move it closer to the client's chair, etc., until the working position feels right for her. Once a correct working position is established, the operator will recognize instantly when she is not correct, and she must alter her position quickly — not continue working under strain. If several staff use one chair position/ epilation cubicle, they must make sure everything is correctly positioned every time they come to work — it only takes a second or two to settle correctly and it is so worthwhile in terms of working comfort.

When setting up business initially it is worth any cost to get the equipment designed specifically for the job; it is likely to earn a lot of money for the operator in a working lifetime, so should not be begrudged. Decide to get the best equipment possible, even if it has to be leased or taken on with extra finance, it will pay in the long term to spend time establishing the ideal working position, chair, stool, and trolley system including the epilation unit, sterilizer, magnifier and storage.

CLIENT HANDLING

With both the client and operator comfortable, the client's skin clean and inspected, equipment checked and ready for use, treatment can start after putting the correct needle into the holder, and switching the epilation unit to the desired intensity for the hair diameter and skin sensitivity.

There is very little to check with the *Beauty Gallery* epilation system, as the on/off switch gives a light which indicates power is available to the unit, and when the needle holder is connected into either outlet, and the switch is depressed, current will flow. A red light above the intensity dial indicates when power is flowing to the needle holder. The amount of current considered a good starting point, or recorded on the treatment card as having proved adequate in the past, can be selected and treatment got under way. It is always a good idea to do one or two hairs in the least sensitive part of the treatment area to let the client settle into the epilation process and adjust to it. Also starting on fairly weak hairs is a kindness to the client and helps to build up her pain capacity. A little bit of careful client handling at this stage can raise the client's pain threshold and extend her treatment tolerance overall, so it is worth being a little thoughtful. Just putting the client at ease, without wasting time, is important to treatment success. Some clients need more help than others, and those with a good pain capacity can almost nod off, especially if cotton-wool pads are used to protect the eyes from the light of the magnifier. Encourage clients to close their eyes, but do not force them to have their eyes covered — some people cannot stand it. Younger clients often prefer to look around and divert their interest, or are interested to see what you are doing. Others prefer not to know, and are just happy to have their problem solved.

Keep a careful check on the actual current used, indicated accurately on the meter of the epilation unit. This provides an actual level of current intensity used to accomplish the result, and this, plus the needle used, and the length of treatment, must be put on the record card at the treatment's conclusion. Always try to use the least current possible; do not simply assume hairs will need a certain level of intensity, just because that is indicated on the client's card. Make your own judgement, as any reduction in current, while maintaining the result, improves the client's pain threshold and capacity for epilation.

Help each client to find her individual way to cope with treatment — being good at client handling is a primary part of being expert at the technique. Luckily, with the advances in epilation treatment developed with the *Beauty Gallery* system, the same discomfort is not experienced as the unit uses less painful frequencies in a special way to reduce reactions in the skin. This breakthrough is a

boon to both the client — who benefits directly — and to the operator — who gains indirectly in having happier clients, and more of them. Causing less pain takes some of the strain out of offering the epilation service. Doing a treatment which causes anxiety and discomfort reflects back to the operator, and electrologists are known for feeling the strain of their work rather personally. Now the pain aspect is greatly reduced, and the number of potential clients that will now be able to cope with epilation treatment is expanded dramatically.

SPACING PROBES

If a fairly small area like the top of the lip is being treated, then probes must be spaced as far apart as is feasible in the circumstances. Do not treat closely associated hairs otherwise it puts the skin under strain, and causes severe reaction which can result in skin damage. Move about the area, for example start at the side lip, working inwards, doing conspicuous hairs first to improve appearance quickly and cheer the client. Do not try to work in the middle of a mass of hairs unless absolutely necessary — as trying to pick the hairs out, even with pointed forceps, is difficult and slow, and if the wrong hair is touched in error, it can be painful for the client. It is faster to work on what can be seen and treated easily — working from the boundaries of the problem, and gradually tackling the difficult, less accessible hairs. Even when the growth is fine and dense and needs a 'thinning out' approach, try to deal with the easier hairs first, as this clears the way to get at the more awkward probes. Making life even more difficult than necessary only results in fewer removals overall, which is not very fair to the client.

If the client has areas of hair well-spaced, such as on the chin, and also has a fine, more dense upper-lip problem, then it makes sense to interspace work on these two areas. This can only be done, however, if the probes can be accomplished using one needle diameter, or if two needle holders with differing needles are available. This method 'rests' the lip and extends the client's capacity for treatment as chin hairs are never as sensitive as the upper-lip area (because of the position of the facial nerve branch in the area). Many highly experienced operators work almost exclusively with one needle diameter, that is a .004 in insulated steel, German needle or Ferrie steel. Their experience and skill in skin handling and control make the need for constant needle changing unnecessary. Probing angle and direction must be absolutely accurate otherwise the follicles will be difficult to enter. A great deal depends on the operator's ability to stretch and control the skin, which makes even a difficult probe possible if the follicle is brought into the ideal position for needle entry.

TREATING THE LIP AND CHIN AREAS

(a) Space the probes carefully on fine, dense, upper-lip hair

(b) Pad the lip area with very thin cotton-wool pieces and soothing lotion after treatment

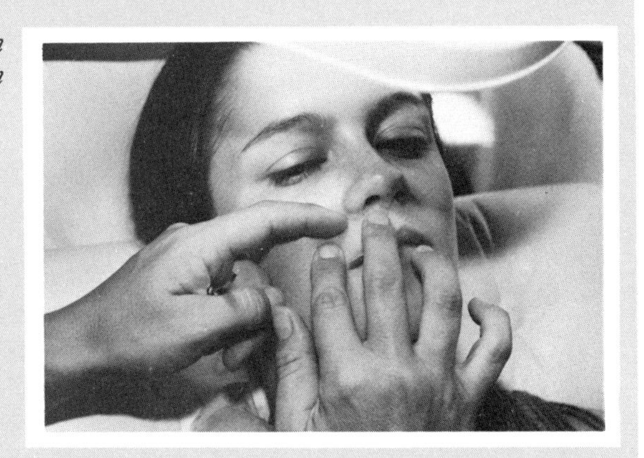

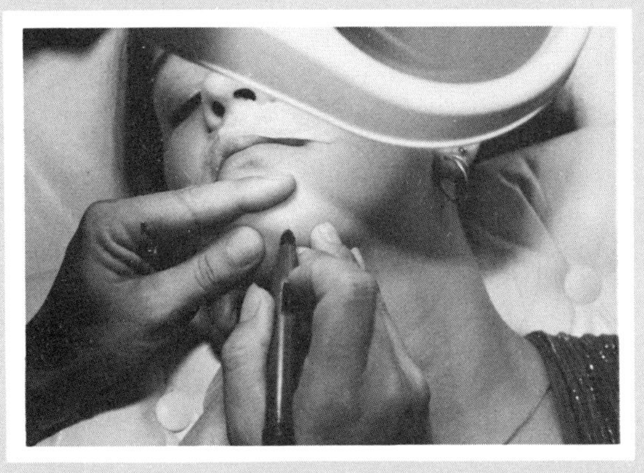

(c) Work in progress on the chin with the lip padded after epilation treatment

If the two areas (the chin and lip) are totally different in character, requiring different needles and current intensity, it can be useful to begin work on the lip, spacing out the probes until the skin's capacity for treatment is used up due to erythema (skin reddening), and then pad this area with very thin layers of cotton wool soaked in cooling solution, while the chin is being treated. This achieves several things: firstly, the skin is cooled and chances of swelling are reduced; secondly, discomfort is decreased as the coolness of the lotion and its anti-inflammatory action get to work to calm the skin and settle nerve endings; finally, healing is promoted. The client goes home with a settled skin, simply dusted with a flesh-tinted camouflaging powder (medicated or azulene-type) or soothing lotion to protect the area of treatment. This 'padding' dramatically improves after-treatment results, and is used extensively in professional electrology. The lotion used must be healing in action, calming and anti-inflammatory, and there are many recipes, most of which are based on natural elements known for their anti-inflammatory actions, such as elderflower water. An azulene gel can also work well as it achieves the same effect of cooling the skin, providing settling elements to the superficial nerve endings, and helps healing in a natural way. What should not be used at this stage of treatment are disinfecting lotions, antiseptics, etc., which have a stimulatory effect; these will cause the skin to smart and increase the blood circulation, at a time when the skin needs to be calm and allowed to start its own healing process. If antiseptic lotions are used during treatment, they must be heavily diluted (proportion of antiseptic lotion to ordinary water should be approximately 1% solution to 99% water). In this way the dilution can help avoid the risk of infection without irritating the skin. Lotions such as Savlon and Cetavlon are useful in a number of ways in the clinic to maintain general hygiene, and can be diluted in different proportions for different tasks.

PADDING THE SKIN

Padding and soothing the skin as you work is one way of extending the skin's, and client's, capacity for treatment. If the skin becomes very red and reacts fiercely, look at your technique and see if an adjustment in current strength, or the method of applying the current, or a change of needle, would be useful. Some clients cope better with a slightly lower current intensity held for fractionally longer on the switch, than with a high intensity applied for a split second. Try both approaches, watch the skin, talk to the client and find out her reaction, and adjust your technique accordingly. Remember the skin may react quickly, but may also calm quickly too, as much of this reaction is a nervous one, so if you calm the person, make them feel secure and in caring hands, their nerves will settle and they will feel calm within themselves.

With the new *Beauty Gallery* epilation system, real pain as such is no longer present in treatment, reactions do not occur to the same extent, but the skin will always react slightly to trauma (shock) and the actual effects of the diathermy; how you help the client to cope with this is all important to overall success.

If, even taking every care, the client does get a strong reaction, think about pre-use of steamers, such as ozone steamers, to disinfect and improve healing in the treatment area. The ozone steam applied for a few minutes prior to and after epilation treatment, and placed about 30 cm (about 12 in) from the facial area to be treated, can help skin that reacts badly, or poor healing skin, or where there is a known skin disturbance such as acne vulgaris or a diabetic condition. The steam helps to such an extent that it may be the only thing that makes epilation treatment possible on these difficult skins, which are liable to break out, become infected after treatment, and show the effects of treatment greatly.

Nowadays, the reaction present from the *Beauty Gallery* epilation system is so reduced compared with previous epilation units that it is now a matter of looking for perfection — but anything that helps reduce the risks of skin marking is worth considering. The most important change overall has been the change in the actual electrical frequencies used within the epilation system itself, this breakthrough making life so much better for the woman with a superfluous hair problem and for the electrologist earning a living helping her resolve this problem.

REDUCING REACTION

To reduce reaction, or avoid it occurring, pay constant attention to your technique and use common sense. Do not work extensively in any one area past the stage where the skin is becoming irritated. Watch the skin as work progresses, and stop when you can see it has had enough — pad up and move on, or rest for a few minutes and work elsewhere for a little while and come back. Alternatively, stop altogether if the skin is showing signs of distress, erythema (redness), swelling, etc., all signs of reaction to the short wave diathermy current application.

Hairs growing closely together in clumps, such as those often seen growing either side of the chin, can cause healing problems if overworked. Do not treat too many hairs in one area during the same treatment session. As the heat reactions converge under the skin, deep healing can be slow if too many removals have been attempted at once. It is better to return on a subsequent treatment, rather than over-treat and have to wait many weeks before the skin can cope with a repeat application. (This treatment planning is all part of epilation technique and is dealt with in depth in *Principles and Techniques for the Electrologist,* by Ann Gallant.)

DEALING WITH DIFFICULT AREAS

Areas of extreme sensitivity call for a rather different approach, and can be 'sneaked' in amongst more comfortable areas, doing a little bit at a time among the more general work. Under the nose can be very trying for the client, as apart from discomfort, it affects the optic nerves, makes the eyes water, brings on a tendency to sneeze in some cases, and generally is not an easy area to treat. Working in rotation helps, popping in a few removals in this area in between the general lip work, and then padding and moving on. Do not persist if the client is really suffering, pick days where her pain capacity is good and her spirits high, then she will cope. Work carefully in these difficult areas, holding carefully, probing very accurately to minimize regrowth potential so that they will not have to be retreated more than necessary. Work for effective results rather than the most removals.

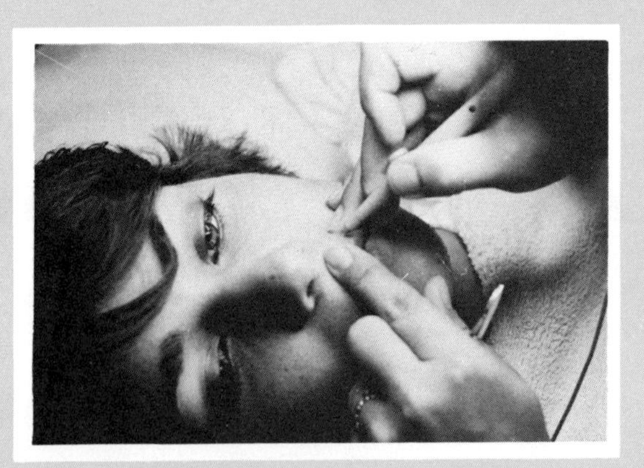

AREAS OF SENSITIVITY

(a) Difficult areas, such as under the nose, must be treated carefully with attention to technique rather than speed of removals

(b) Avoid surface burns at all costs by keeping the hand steady

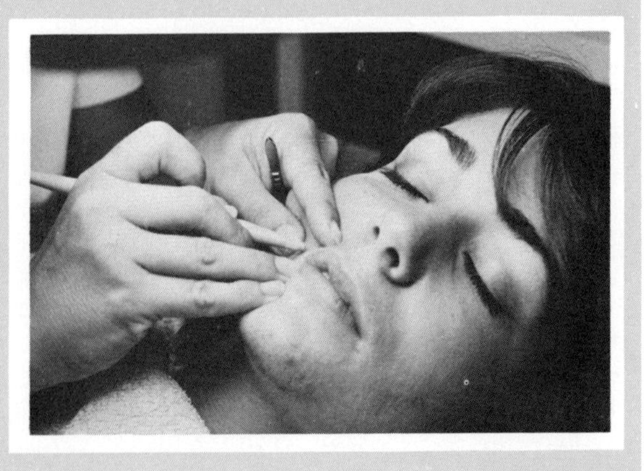

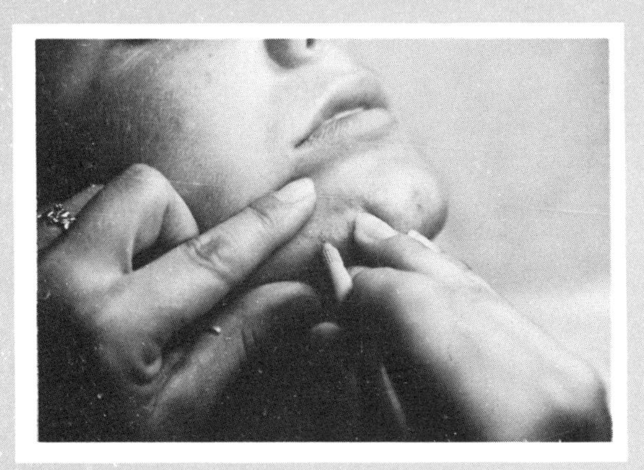

(c) Use the minimum current possible and get the probe depth correct

ADJUSTING THE CURRENT

Do not forget to adjust the power on the epilation unit while treatment is in progress if you need to. Have the unit where it can be easily reached for minute current adjustments where needed. It can sometimes be better to adjust the current rather than prolong or shorten the tap on the switch control. While it is not sensible to adjust the current for each probe, the epilation unit should become like an extension of the hand, and adjustments made as a matter of course when needed. Likewise, the positioning of the magnifier must become almost like a part of the operator's eyes, helping her to see from the best possible angle and with maximum illumination of the treatment area.

Work should be swift, efficient, and free from strain and the operator should be able to stay and work at her position for long hours, feeling comfortable and in control of her equipment.

USE THE BEST EQUIPMENT AVAILABLE

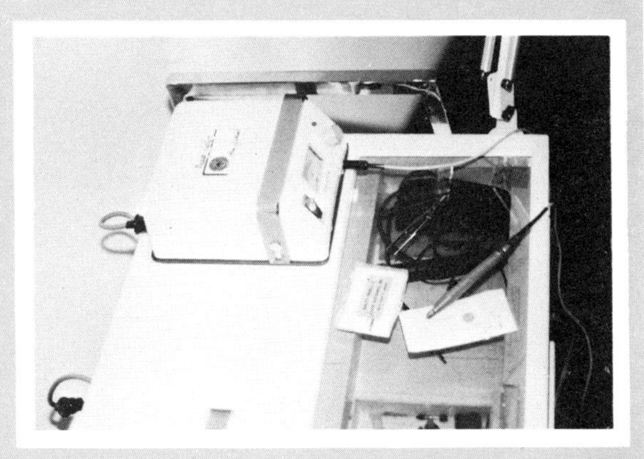

AFTER-CARE ADVICE

When the skin seems to have had enough treatment, or the appointment period is over, the skin can be wiped over and final checks for annoying and 'offending' hairs completed. A quick look all around the area of treatment, using the magnifier's light to 'throw up the hairs' and catch any odd, strong, or very obvious hairs that attract attention and worry the client, can be completed. These can be dealt with speedily, making the client feel as tidy as possible, and avoids the temptation of plucking.

The skin can be protected with medicated soothing lotion, tinted medicated or azulene powder, or antiseptic cream of a non-irritant type. Azulene gels can also be used. The client must be reminded of home-care measures before she leaves and can then be tidied up, protective tissue removed, and general appearance checked for odd bits of cotton wool, powder, etc. She may then be helped from the chair and can be given a new appointment, or be told when to make it for when she reaches the reception desk. If there is any doubt whether the client will be ready for further treatment at the next suggested appointment date, then she should be asked to telephone in for an appointment when she thinks she is ready, or pop in for a quick inspection to see if her skin is up to further treatment.

TREATMENT BOOKING

The client should be encouraged to keep regular appointments — it helps move progress forwards. If the client comes a long distance and if there is a possibility that her skin might be found unsuitable for further treatment, it is preferable to over-space treatment dates initially until her reactions are known; this will save her the inconvenience of travelling in unnecessarily. Two weeks is a normal treatment gap for hairs in the same immediate area. Naturally, clients with a more extensive hair problem can have their treatment in rotation, so be prepared to provide treatment when needed, but let the skin itself dictate the overall pattern of treatment application and spacing.

As the client is getting herself ready to leave, her record card can be filled in with the treatment details — date, length, area of treatment, etc., which takes a few seconds only and is important to business efficiency. If the client later telephones to make an appointment, it must be on record when she last came, how long her appointment was, which areas were treated, her reactions, progress, etc. It is not always possible, simply by looking at the skin, to know when the previous epilation treatment was completed. The skin may look settled and ready for further treatment, but underlying tissues which take longer to heal than

surface skin layers may not be healed. These deeper layers are the ones which have been subjected to the bulk of the destructive diathermy current.

The client's next appointment can be booked, either by the operator if working on her own, or at the reception by the client (though in this case the operator should advise the client on a suitable date). It is helpful when running a busy practice to have a shared reception, or a person wholly responsible for appointment bookings and answering the telephone, otherwise telephone calls, etc., will constantly interrupt the actual epilation application, disrupting the flow of work, and not giving an opportunity for an adequate amount of epilation to be completed.

Many clinic practices have regular clients who book on a regular fortnightly basis, and know exactly when they are coming, they simply confirm their next appointment as they pay for their treatment.

Most of the operator's work will centre around facial electrology, and this valuable service is a very worthwhile and profitable — if demanding — one to offer. With the very best of equipment and knowledge, the potential is there for an excellent career in electrology.

9

Hair facts — check your knowledge

Q. **How is hair classified?**
A. Hair can be classified as three main types.

(1) *Lanugo hair,* fetal hair (hair of unborn child in the womb), usually dark.
(2) *Vellus hair,* very soft, short, often blonde or lacking pigment (depending on the individual's colouring), downy facial/body hair.
(3) *Terminal hair,* coarser, visible, longer, usually pigmented (coloured).

Q. **How is lanugo hair different from vellus hair?**
A. Lanugo hair is the first hair formed in the follicle, from the pre-germinal stage of the hair as it develops in the unborn child. It seems to have a special role as often this hair is shed before birth or soon afterwards. It is quite common for babies to be born with a head of dense soft fine hair, which can also grow down on to their foreheads and low on their necks. This hair soon falls out and is replaced with very fine *vellus hairs,* which may be rather insignificant and lacking pigment. Many babies wait a long time for their permanent hair, which indicates the complex structure of the hair follicle, and how it is subject to changes or forces of activity in the body. So the term 'lanugo' only relates to fetal hair, and is incorrect for hair found on older children or adults. Its classification or description comes from where it grew — not its appearance.

Q. **Why do textbooks still talk of lanugo hair when they really mean vellus hair? It can be confusing for the student.**
A. Hair and its relationship to physical health has become an area of increased medical interest and the terms relating to hair have become more precise. It is now common knowledge that hair is an excellent indicator of what is happening within the body, and that people, although they do not die from their unwanted hair, can actually become ill from the cause of it. So it is now necessary to strive for accuracy in the terminology of hair. The terms lanugo and vellus have now acquired their own special meanings. Older

publications still interchange the terms, but the electrology profession, having a specialized knowledge in the field, should strive for accuracy, following the medical lead.

Q. **Terminal hairs and vellus hairs, how are they different?**
A. The simple answer would be to say, terminal hairs are coarse, long and normally dark or pigmented; vellus hairs are short, soft, downy and normally colourless. This is not the whole story however, and terminal and vellus hairs will be found together in many parts of the body, such as the scalp and the back (in men).

For example, hairs of the scalp are usually longer than those of the back, and are known as terminal hairs. Vellus hairs are also present on the scalp, and terminal hairs of the back may be very similar in looks to the vellus or finer hairs of the scalp. So it is the length and coarseness of a hair in relation to the area where it is found that determines the term terminal.

When hypertrichosis (excessive unwanted hair for the area) is described, often hairs are talked about as being terminal in nature; that is they have grown out of character for the area, and are abnormal in relation to their normal or expected appearance. Breast hairs are a typical case; hairs around the nipple, which change from vellus to coarse and terminal-like hair, do so because of hormone influences.

There are very real differences between vellus and terminal hairs. Vellus hairs have short active growing phases and long resting periods, in other words they have a fast replacement system and stay put a long time. Terminal hairs have a longer anagen phase (growing period) and a relatively shorter telogen phase. Perhaps this is because there are more permanent structures to form in the follicle, more hair plus associated units to form the philo-sebaceous unit, and this compared with the less significant vellus hair takes longer to accomplish. So the terminal hair takes longer to form, and is not static for as long. It has a more active growth rate (as epilation of leg hairs will show), nearly all hairs being removed at some stage of the anagen phase. The papilla of the vellus hair does not have a strong blood supply, just a few capillaries are present surrounding the lower end of the follicle. No vessels penetrate into the dermal papilla, and here we come to another difference in character. Terminal follicles are intermeshed with vascular blood vessels encircling the entire lower two-thirds of the follicle, with some blood vessels entering the very active dermal papilla itself. It is this vascularity that needs to be destroyed with permanent hair removal, for it is the follicle's life-support system, carrying messages to the hair follicle relating to growth, etc. Vellus hair follicles lie in the surface of the skin, very shallow — 1 mm deep only — and terminal hairs are deeper — up to 4 to 5 mm deep

sometimes. The danger of surface burns in the treatment of vellus hairs is obvious, because of the close proximity to the dry surface tissues. Vellus hairs lack a medulla, but terminal hairs normally have one present.

When vellus hairs change in nature from downy, simple structures, to stronger, more complex, terminal structures, the change is heralded through the blood supply by hormone messages. The follicle becomes deeper, capable of supporting a stronger hair with its need for greater nutrients from the blood vessels. The intermeshed vascularity forms to support the follicle and its contents — the hair — and from that point on the follicle remains unchanged in form, and seldom regresses (that is by changing and becoming weaker, or going back to its vellus state). So the change from vellus to terminal is likely to be permanent.

Q. **What are vibrissae hairs?**
A. Vibrissae hairs are highly specialized tactile hairs on all mammals, except humans, sometimes called whiskers, which surround the eyes, lips or muzzles of animals. These hair follicles are surrounded by many nerves and are well-supplied with erectile-like tissue. Humans do not have this form of follicle so it is incorrect to use the term in relation to them. It should only be used in relation to the animal world.

Q. **What are the stages in the hair growth cycle?**
A. (1) *Anagen* — actively growing phase.
(2) *Catagen* — transitional or changing phase.
(3) *Telogen* — resting phase.

Q. **How do you know a hair is in the anagen phase?**
A. The hair is actively growing, and attains its greatest potential length in the anagen phase. Several structures or parts of the hair root are clearly visible, and can be described as follows.

The anagen hair, can be described as having an upper portion or *shaft,* and a lower portion which is the *bulb.* The bulb is considered as having an *upper bulb area,* and a lower part termed the *matrix.* The definitions relate to the different functions, roles or activities that the hair has in different areas, that is, areas of greatest mitotic activity, transition into keratinized hair, acquiring pigment cells, becoming hard and losing fluid (hard keratinization stage).

Different things occur at different places in the follicle, and this can be traced or defined as follows.
Inner root sheath grows upwards towards the skin's surface, covering the lower two-thirds of the hair shaft, like a wrapping or bandage.
Outer root sheath surrounds the hair from the pilary canal down to the bottom of the bulb. It overlies the inner root sheath.
Dermal papilla is surrounded by the bulb and forms an area of connective tissue deep inside its structure. The whole bulb is

composed of cells in active stages of cellular growth and transition. Indeed the entire bulb and matrix areas and lower follicle need to be involved with the epilation process for the follicle's growth capacity to be successfully destroyed or impaired, minimizing the regrowth of hairs.

Basal lamina is a non-cellular membrane, separating the papilla from the cells of the bulb, and it also continues up around the bulb, separating the outer root sheath from the connective tissue sheath. *Connective tissue sheath* surrounds the follicle and merges into the dermis close to the skin's surface. Each of the follicle's layers seems to have a specialized role to perform, in the initial and sustained growth of the hair, and they are possibly all related to changes occurring in the growth cycle as the hair moves from anagen to telogen and repeats the renewal process.

Q. **What is the telogen hair follicle like?**

A. The hair is simpler in form, termed a 'club hair', where the shaft section ends without a bulb, but is either blunt or pointed at its end. Being at a resting stage, the follicle is short, closer to the surface, and is at a lower stage of mitotic activity. Hairs epilated at this stage may leave behind a follicle capable of renewed life, when the correct messages are received from the body's endocrine system via the blood stream.

Remnants of the inner root sheath, which have collapsed, are wrapped around the hair like a skirt, with the free hem or skirt edge embedded into the surrounding connective tissue. The inner root sheath waits to become active again, and is folded away until needed.

The germ capsule is composed chiefly of the remnants or remaining cells of the outer sheath, encapulating or surrounding the base of the club hair (giving it the strange blob or full stop appearance). Strands or rootlets coming from the germ capsule help anchor the club hair into the follicle.

A new papilla lies at the base, outside and lower down below the older follicle which previously grew the club hair just being shed.

Q. **At the anagen stage of growth, what areas of the hair follicle need to be destroyed to minimize regrowth?**

A. Depending on the strength of the actual hair, and hormone influences, it is normally considered that the lower two-thirds of the follicle, including the hair bulb, the connective tissue sheath, the papilla, and the mitotically active area surrounding the lower bulb/matrix have to be destroyed. This includes coagulating the small blood vessels threading themselves like a tiny fretwork around the follicle base, for without this destruction the follicle can recharge and build new hairs of equal strength again. If hairs are of exceptional vigour, like some leg hairs, it may be preferable to give adequate levels of current intensity for fractionally longer

durations, to ensure the follicle is destroyed. In this way there is time for the correct type of cellular destruction to take place. Very high, short sharp bursts of current can leave an active follicle with too much regrowth potential, and so a slower, lower approach is needed with the correct application. Here the new advanced systems of epilation are beneficial, for they reduce pain, while allowing the destructive and necessary element of current to do its work, causing resistance from the tissues which destroys the follicle's growth potential. Achieving this on strong follicles without skin damage is an art.

Q. **Is a treated telogen hair follicle likely to regenerate a new hair?**
A. If the tissue below the club hair, that is the germ capsule, and beyond, to the new or nude papilla is correctly treated, then regrowth is likely to be minimal while the follicle is in this susceptible state. Because of lack of recognition, however, the follicle is often treated in a shallow fashion; the club hair blocks the needle's passage down the follicle, and the slightly deeper probe is missed. The new hair forms from the recharged follicle, strong as ever, or just a bit distorted because of damage to the tissue sheaths or forming papilla.

Q. **If an inadequate amount of current needed for a perfect destruction has been used, or the correct parts of the follicle have not been reached, when will regrowth emerge from the skin?**
A. It depends on the error, and the stage of the hair follicle at the time of treatment. Over-shallow probes, which have injured or broken off only the superficial part of the hair shaft will result in blunt, damaged hairs emerging from the skin in 2 to 7 days. If the hair was treated during the telogen phase, but the new papilla missed, the new hair has first to receive its message to rejuvenate, then it has to grow towards the surface and emerges to be visible 6 weeks to 3 months later (the time of year does make a difference here). If an anagen hair was 'eased out' or the slight resistance really was a 'tug', then the follicle will recover, and depending on the client's hair condition and body influences (that is, the extent of her hair problem or causes of hypertrichosis or hirsutism), then the hair will reappear in 3 to 6 weeks. This is a hair treated but not destroyed and may replace itself very quickly. Many people consider that strong anagen hairs need thorough, careful treatment, with the current acting right up to the isthmus area of the follicle if regrowth is to be minimized. It certainly points to using techniques that achieve the most successful removals, rather than concentrating on the number of hairs removed. Be sure to use enough current, as strong hairs in healthy skin areas need adequate destruction if repeated regrowth is to be avoided. Try to keep in

mind 'best results overall' as the judge for the technique needed, and what is needed to accomplish the task well.

Excessive regrowth may have lots of causes, for example hormone condition, drug inducement (such as with fertility drugs, etc.), or be the result of natural factors such as in the male awaiting sex-change surgery, where the hair growth will be excessive until hormone therapy and surgery start to have an effect. Causes are many, but if there appears to be no background for the problem, it can nearly always be traced to faulty technique.

Q. **Is regrowth an inevitable part of professional electrology because of skin limitations, and how can you distinguish between acceptable regrowth and that relating to faulty technique?**
A. Regrowth is not an inevitable part of electrology, and far too much is accepted as being so, but there are times when skin limitations or excessive growth make it difficult to avoid if the skin is to survive and not be marked. Always aim for minimal regrowth, even if it means working fractionally slower — permanent removal is the overall aim. Unless hairs are receiving exceptional stimuli from physical factors within the body, they should not regrow more than twice. Further regrowths need investigation — a new approach, perhaps updating to a new method, or some deep thinking or refreshing of techniques through training. Often a careful analysis of the work, looking at regrowths closely, not drifting along in old habits may be needed. Most remedies lie in the operator's hands.

A 'normal' regrowth hair from a strong anagen hair follicle will be lighter in colour, sometimes translucent, and altered in structure; the hair bulb will be less deeply placed, not containing such a well-formed viscose sheath covering around the bulb — i.e. the normal regrowth hair is less deep, less strong, less coloured, sometimes distorted, but distinctly weakened compared with the original hair.

Q. **How can I recognize and correct my insertion technique causing excessive regrowth, as I want to do the best for my client?**
A. Study the anatomy of the hair follicle really well from books such as *Principles and Techniques for the Electrologist,* by Ann Gallant. See how the hair forms, renews itself and the stimuli it responds to via the blood stream. Know the enemy and make a plan. Also look carefully at hairs, normal ones that fall out from the scalp, lashes, etc., or get pulled out accidentally or plucked out on purpose. See the differences when a hair is discarded naturally or is pulled out alive. Hairs are wonderfully structured, anchored in by their concentric sheaths and follicle attachments.

Measure an epilated hair against your needle and see how short it really is; match it against an insulated needle's exposed area, and you can see that the needle manufacturers know a lot about the

'enemy'. Few hairs are more deeply placed than the shiny exposed area of the insulated probe tip, just a couple of millimetres deep. The same goes for the pointed tip of the one-piece tapered steel needle, which measures approximately .003 to .004 in diameter or the tip of the two-piece Ferrie needle in a bigger shank or base; they both have either a constant diameter along the entire needle section and only the tip is pointed, or the entire needle is graduated from base to point. Only the tip enters the skin, and although the entire needle is important as it carries the current and takes the strain, only the tip reacts against the skin tissues of the follicle, and current must accurately reach all parts of the hair follicle for destruction. So check the follicle depth, needle depth, and remember that if hairs are in anagen, the base of the follicle must be reached, but not over-shot. Sense of touch helps; avoid both over-shallow probes (hairs emerge very quickly, 3 to 5 days, and areas need repeated clearing) and over-deep probes, where the active papilla area is only partially destroyed, and regrows much as before, the hair is eased out, or current used excessively to compensate, causing white ringing, over-reaction, skin damage, marking and possible scarring. Work initially to find out the correct probe depth, insertion level and ideal current intensity. Take care over this, as it sets the success of the entire programme.

Remember that the types of hair can be very mixed in an area. There may be regrowth and virgin hairs in the same area, and technique has to rely very much on 'feel' and 'sense of touch'. Very few hairs, even when the client has a genetic or hormone problem, lie deeper in the skin than 2 mm; few exceed one-third of the length of a two-piece Ferrie-type needle, many much less (the exposed tip of the insulated needle is just over 1 mm and the rest insulated down the needle length, therefore the skin's surface will be protected if the follicle is a deep one).

Take the longest hair available, place it alongside your needle, and see how it matches up. If the needle goes in deeper than the hair follicle, it coagulates deep blood vessels not belonging to the hair follicle itself, so although the skin is damaged, the hair itself will not lift without resistance from the follicle. Hair removal will be poor and the follicle will regrow a new hair in time.

The follicle acts as the restraining element to the needle, and electrologists, if given time to train and gain necessary experience, begin to sense the resistance of the base of the follicle which tells them they are in the right place. This information can be confirmed by checking the length and structure of the initial hairs removed, and being aware of regrowth and progress of treatment. It is known that there is more to it than this, for example overgrowth of tissue sheaths, oily blockage causing messy removals as it sticks to the needle and deflects the power of the current on the

tissues, distorted follicles, impacted hairs, and excessive hormone influence from the body. All these factors can be overcome, if attention to overall technique is given throughout.

Poor insertions are not the only cause of excessive regrowth, getting the current to the right place, using enough current long enough, *being accurate* is the name of the game.

Q. **Insertions seem deep and accurate, but the client still gets regrowth. How do I know if this is due to faults in my technique, or could be related to hormone factors in the client?**
A. If the client shows no obvious reasons for presenting such difficulty in treatment, such as a medical condition needing drug medication, for example, for sub-fertility, or HRT (hormone replacement therapy) especially in the younger woman, or use of the 'Pill' over a long period, etc., then a faulty technique is normally the cause. If the client does not know her exact state of health, and the problem is really severe, do ask her to check with her doctor, for occasionally there may be a cause that is not immediately evident, but one which could be discovered with more detailed medical investigation — conditions such as a cyst on the ovary or a tumour affecting the performance of glands in the endocrine system, etc. Anyone with a poor gynaecological history should always have detailed counselling from the electrologist, and medical help sought if considered at all necessary. Do not alarm the client, but do not try to work in isolation if you feel a problem exists.

Having eliminated related causes, let us look at faulty technique and its effect on the anagen follicle again. Deep or over-deep probes with inadequate follicle destruction can cause anagen follicles to move swiftly to replace the lost hair. The follicle appears to go into premature telogen, then anagen in all its stages follows on immediately and an identical strength hair is formed.

The follicle has to discard the structures relating to the normal anagen hair just removed (but not destroyed). Often termed 'tombstone' hairs because of their strange appearance, these are perhaps premature telogen hair fragments being expelled by the follicle in preparation for building a new hair. Repeating tombstones or simply too many repeats and little progress or remission, indicate a need to scrutinize the depths of the probes into the follicle. If treatment had been accurate and adequate, the hairs would have been removed and destroyed, and no further growth activity could occur in that follicle.

If these hairs were actually new growths — vellus hairs changed in form to a stronger terminal-type — no distortion or tombstone hairs would be seen. If it was new terminal hair developing due to strong hormone forces circulating in the blood stream affecting

these target sensitive hairs, it would appear like any other natural-looking hairy growth which develops in a previously untreated area.

Hairs with an unusual distorted form, or those that are impacted (growing back inside the follicle), or growing along under the skin's surface as they clear the follicle mouth, can all appear in clients from incorrect techniques or faulty treatment. They are also seen on new clients as they commence treatment, and are due to previous home measures like plucking, waxing, etc. If a reason for their presence is not obvious, faulty technique has to be considered.

Q. **The hair has a shaft section and a root area. What are the three layers of the hair shaft?**

A. (1) *Medulla* — the central innermost part or layer of the hair. Hair tone and colour is affected by large air spaces in the medulla.

(2) *Cortex* — between the outer layer of the hair and the central medulla. It forms the bulk of the hair and contains the pigment melanin in dark hair.

(3) *Cuticle* — Outermost layer formed of a single layer of scales with the free margins directed towards the tip of the hair. Scales are translucent and non-pigmented. The cuticle binds the cortex; without this protection the hair becomes frayed and split. Split ends come about as a result of drying elements and strong chemical damage to the hair, breaking up the protective action of the cuticle. Hair conditioners smooth the cuticle of the hair, making it feel instantly smooth and tangle free.

Q. **What purpose does the medulla have and is it present in all hairs?**

A. The medulla is present in coarser terminal hairs but absent in vellus hairs. Its purpose is rather obscure but its absence in downy hair may indicate that its role is connected with overall strength. Even finer terminal hairs such as on children do not have a visible medulla except through an electron-microscope (many times more magnification than an ordinary light microscope). Hairs with a medulla are termed *medullated,* and without a medulla, *non-medullated;* so lanugo hair is non-medullated, as is vellus hair. Terminal hair may or may not be according to its coarseness.

Q. **Why is the hair bulb divided into sections when described?**

A. Because this enables the descriptions to relate to the role or purpose of each area, (1) Upper base — the upper portion of the enlarged base, (2) Matrix — lower portion of the bulb; germination centre of the anagen follicle, (3) Critical level — the transitionary 'imaginary line' drawn across the widest part or

diameter of the dermal papilla. It is said that below this dividing line lies the matrix, above it is the upper bulb. It is a convenient way of telling where critical and important changes or events take place within the hair bulb.

Q. **What is the special role of the matrix?**
A. Here the life force of the hair occurs, it is where the hair actually comes from, so it is vital to understand when striving for perfect electrology technique. New hair cells develop from cell division (mitosis) in the matrix, and as they grow they move upwards from the matrix, change shape and form to become recognizable hairs. The hair cells change from round to elongated forms, acquire pigment colour, and develop keratin which causes them to lose moisture and become hard. They then emerge from the skin's surface as a hair shaft.

The matrix is the growing centre of the forming anagen hair follicle, so its capacity to function must be destroyed with the electrology application, even if it cannot be achieved in one application because of the possibility of excessive skin damage to surrounding tissues. During catagen, the matrix disintegrates and a new matrix forms with the next anagen phase, so the matrix and its follicle, and the hair they produce, all live and die together. This is why the unit must always be thought of as one. The bulb is the only part of the hair where the cells are alive. Once the hair cells move up beyond the bulb, they are completely keratinized and dead. So cutting hairs or shaving them can never stimulate hair growth, dead hairs cannot react. Waxing/plucking can alter hair growth in some cases, as the follicle reacts to the injury and can quickly replace a lost hair. It does seem, on occasion, that continuous plucking actually induces the hair follicle to become more viable and able to build a very good vascular supply to build replacement hairs within the follicle, perhaps as a response to the injury caused.

Q. **What are the tissues that grow from the matrix to form the hair?**
A. Six different structures grow from the matrix. Hair tissue — composed of medulla, cortex and cuticle. Inner root sheath — cuticle of inner root sheath, Huxley's layer and Henle's layer (these layers gain their names from the scientists who were first to discern and identify the different layers as separate structures).

Q. **Is the inner root sheath ever visible?**
A. On certain occasions it can be seen but only when epilated. It disintegrates inside the hair follicle before the hair shaft emerges from the skin's surface. If a hair is epilated at just too low a level of current and is a less than perfect removal or is given a gentle tug, or is actually plucked, white tissue can sometimes be seen adhering to

a portion of the hair. This is the inner root sheath. Occasionally it actually turns inside out like a translucent sleeve, and as the epilated hair is removed it lies on the skin's surface like a little empty tube.

Q. **What is keratin?**
A. Keratin is a protein formed in the epidermis, nails and hair. It is the substance which hardens the hair cells so that when the hair emerges from the skin, it is hard and flexible, and not soft, moist or gel-like, similar to cells from the hair bulb. Examine an epilated hair closely, and see at what point the soft gel-like consistency becomes hard along its shaft, and the hair becomes less flexible. Holding the hair in the forceps, test its flexibility by putting the bulb section, with its milky-looking sheath, on to a hard surface. See at what point it becomes more rigid. This shows the start of the keratinization zone, where the hair cells give up moisture, changing form and becoming keratinized and hard.

Q. **What actually is keratinization?**
A. It is the process or series of changes that cells go through, as they change from germ cells (produced in the matrix of the hair bulb) to hair shaft cells. When hair cells move up from the bulb to the hair shaft, they change from soft round gelatinous structures, to elongated, hard, fibre-like structures, more rod-like in appearance. As they progress upwards and move up the shaft, they lose more and more fluid, becoming more and more keratinized, until they become totally without fluid — keratinized and dead cells.

Q. **How is it that different structures containing keratin, such as the inner root sheath and epidermis, are softer than hair itself? Does keratin come in different types?**
A. Yes. There are considered to be two types of keratin, soft and hard keratin. Hair and nails complete the whole process and undergo hard keratinization, whereas skin and inner root sheath undergo soft keratinization.

Q. **What role does keratin play in the epidermis of the skin?**
A. Keratinized cells cover and help protect the outside of the body from minor injury, and they hinder the penetration of micro-organisms and harmful solvents, strong chemicals, etc. They also help reduce the evaporation of body fluids. Cells formed in the basal layer of the skin move upwards towards the surface, losing fluid and becoming flattened and horny in the process. Keratinized cells are not found in the dermis, only the epidermis.

Q. **What is melanin?**
A. Melanin is a pigment occurring in human tissue, and is responsible for the colour of the skin and hair. It is either brown or black and is formed in the cytoplasm of special cells called melanocytes.

Q. **Where are the melanocytes located in the skin?**
A. Melanocytes are found in the junction between the epidermis and the dermis. They are also found in the junction between the papilla and the hair bulb.

Q. **How does the melanin move from the cytoplasm of the melanocyte to the hair?**
A. The melanocyte can change its shape, and by sending out a finger-like projection, it can directly inject its melanin granules into the new hair cells while they are still soft (before they have become hardened and keratinized). These finger-like projections are called *dendrites,* and melanocyte cells are said to be dendritic cells.

Q. **Does all hair tissue have melanin?**
A. No, only the cortex of the hair has melanin, it is not found in the cuticle or medulla. Also white hair has no pigment, or has lost it; so melanin stops forming for some reason, as yet unknown.

Q. **Are there any special problems of applying electrology on coloured skin?**
A. Coloured skin is itself rather different in its reaction to epilation, even when applied well and with every regard to careful technique. Skin seems very prone to hyperpigmentation (dark colouration after heat diathermy) and can become almost black in colour, giving the appearance of a birthmark on occasions; so it is difficult to treat, can be slow to heal, is prone to severe reactions on occasion, and can mark badly if tremendous care is not taken in its treatment. It is not known why the coloured skin is so prone to scarring (especially with reference to keloid scarring); all that the electrologist can do to minimize the risk is to take special care on overall technique. Treatment should be completed with the very minimum current possible and the use of an insulated needle if possible (that is a Ferrie steel needle, with insulation material up the main part of its length, leaving only the actual tip exposed). The insulated needle keeps the main activity of the destructive current at the root area of the follicle and prevents the spread of the current upwards to the same degree as a traditional needle, thus reducing erythema effects on the drier surface skin tissue, where marking would occur. Great care should be given to probes being accurately angled and inserted to the correct depth into the follicle, so that surface burns do not occur. It is preferable to work slowly and carefully to ensure that each application is as effective as possible, leading to minimum regrowth. This does not mean that more current can be employed than the skin can cope with (which is always the overriding guidance in treatment) but rather that each probe should be really effective and that speed in itself is not the most important factor. Special attention should be given to pre-care (use of ozone vapour steaming if available), use of soothing lotions and skin padding during treatment (based on

anti-inflammatory elements such as elderflower lotion), and correct after-care, healing creams, powders or protective pastes to avoid the risk of infection which could occur from careless skin hygiene. Ozone steaming can be used to advantage both before and after the routine, and can be costed into the treatment charge.

Treatments should be given for short durations, and be spaced well apart (two or three weeks if the skin is very sensitive). Probes should be well spaced to avoid overlapping heat reactions which could cause hyperpigmentation to occur. Prior to each treatment the skin should be very carefully inspected to ensure that deep healing has taken place, and if not, these areas should be avoided, or the treatment delayed for a little longer. The correct pattern of treatment organization — spacing, timing, treatment duration, and correct technique — for these more difficult skins soon emerges, and if the electrologist also makes her client aware of the part she plays in achieving a good result, overall success will be assured.

HAIR FACTS — QUICK TEST 1

(1) What is mitosis?
- (a) pigment/colour formation
- (b) cell division
- (c) a process by which hair becomes hard and loses fluid

(2) Where is the hair born?
- (a) papilla/matrix
- (b) upper bulb
- (c) critical layer
- (d) hair shaft

(3) In anagen which sections of the follicle need to be destroyed for successful epilation to occur?
- (a) lower two-thirds of the follicle and surrounding tiny blood vessels
- (b) bulb area only
- (c) dermal papilla only
- (d) entire follicle
- (e) upper half of the follicle

(4) A hair has to contain melanin to be healthy. True or false?

(5) A club hair is found in the
- (a) telogen stage.
- (b) catagen stage.
- (c) anagen stage.

(6) Melanocyte is the name of a type of
  (a) cell.
  (b) hair.
  (c) skin.

(7) Keratinized cells are found in the dermis. True or false?

(8) The finger-like projections of the melanocyte are called
  (a) keratin.
  (b) dendrites.
  (c) melanin.

(9) Melanocytes are cells found in the
  (a) dermis and the epidermis.
  (b) junction between the dermis and the epidermis.
  (c) inner root sheath.

(10) As the keratinization process occurs, hairs lose
  (a) cells.
  (b) colour.
  (c) moisture.

(Answers to Test 1 on page 85.)

HAIR FACTS — QUICK TEST 2

(1) The substance which hardens nails, skin and hair is
  (a) carbohydrate.
  (b) keratin.
  (c) melanin.

(2) Keratin gives hair its colour. True or false?

(3) Keratin is found only in the bulb of the hair. True or false?

(4) The keratinization process occurs only in the hair. True or false?

(5) The pigment which is responsible for the colour of human hair and skin is
  (a) telogen.
  (b) keratin.
  (c) melanin.
  (d) melanocytes.

(6) Vellus hairs are found in human adults. True or false?

(7) Vibrissae hairs are found in
  (a) cats.
  (b) babies.
  (c) adult humans.

(8) Vellus hairs have a medulla. True or false?

(9) Lanugo hairs are found in adults. True or false?

(10) Vellus hairs have a
- (a) long anagen phase and no telogen phase.
- (b) short anagen phase and no telogen phase.
- (c) short anagen phase and relatively long telogen phase.
- (d) long anagen phase and long telogen phase.

(Answers to Test 2 on page 85.)

HAIR FACTS — QUICK TEST 3

(1) The three layers of a hair shaft are
- (a) matrix, vibrissae, papilla.
- (b) medulla, cortex, cuticle.

(2) All human hairs have three layers. True or false?

(3) The stages of the hair growth cycle are
- (a) dermal, papilla, catagen, telogen.
- (b) anagen, catagen, telogen.
- (c) vellus, lanugo, vibrissae.

(4) The hair bulb is present only during the ________ phase of the hair growth cycle.

(5) If you make a very shallow insertion into a deep terminal hair follicle you might succeed in permanently destroying that follicle. True or false?

(6) List three structures that are present in an anagen hair follicle.

(7) The critical layer is an imaginary line that divides the bulb into the
- (a) papilla and matrix.
- (b) upper bulb and papilla.
- (c) upper bulb and matrix.

(8) Hair growth occurs from the
- (a) outer root sheath.
- (b) inner root sheath.
- (c) hair bulb.

(9) The inner root sheath grows from the
- (a) outer root sheath.
- (b) papilla.
- (c) matrix.

(10) Common causes of white ringing are
- (a) excessive current.
- (b) over-deep probes.
- (c) over-shallow probes.
- (d) needle movement at discharge of current.

(11) Common causes of excessive regrowth are
- (a) incorrect probe depth.
- (b) insufficient current used.
- (c) use of wrong needle diameter.
- (d) excessive use of current.

(12) Long-term effects of over-treatment are
- (a) pitting.
- (b) scarring.
- (c) weeping follicles.
- (d) blistering and white ringing.
- (e) excessive regrowth.
- (f) pigmentation changes.

(13) Immediate signs of over-treatment are
- (a) erythema.
- (b) swelling.
- (c) blanching.
- (d) scabs.
- (e) infection.
- (f) scars.

Answers Test 1

(1) b. (2) a. (3) a. (4) False. (5) a. (6) a. (7) False. (8) b. (9) b. (10) c.

Answers Test 2

(1) b. (2) False. (3) False. (4) False. (5) c. (6) True. (7) a. (8) False. (9) False. (10) c.

Answers Test 3

(1) b. (2) False. (3) b. (4) Anagen. (5) False. (6) Hair Inner root sheath. Outer root sheath. Basal lamina. Connective tissue sheath. (7) c. (8) c. (9) c. (10) a, c, d. (11) a, b. (12) a, b, f. (13) a, b, c.

10

Essential facts about sterilization

THE RESPONSIBILITY

The electrologist has never had a greater need than now for proper methods of sterilization, with the increased risks of hepatitis B, AIDS and herpes that are present. Old methods are simply not sufficient to stand up against these new virulent strains of bacteria and micro-organisms, and although the traditional means of cleansing and sterilizing still play a part — and a very essential one — it is now necessary to take further measures to combat the risks of cross-infection.

If the old methods of sterilization are considered, it is easy to see why they are no longer adequate. It was thought that high-frequency current was enough to sterilize the needle tip itself, but this was not in fact correct, as the levels of heat produced were not sustained long enough, or high enough. Some of the older, stronger machines did have a 'testing' outlet, which could be used at a high intensity for 30 seconds, with the needle placed in the outlet, and finger or foot control pressed down for the entire period. Even here this would not have been sufficient power against the new viral strains such as hepatitis B, which requires a different approach to kill completely. Nowadays, modern epilation machines do not use the same frequencies as they once did; comfort is improved for the client, but the high levels of heat/diathermy are with us no more so no sterilizing of this kind can take place.

In fact, because of the different blends of current now used to produce the more effective and comfortable treatment, there does exist a risk of taking bacteria into the follicle on the needle, where it finds a beautifully moist and warm environment in which to grow and cause trouble. Picked up via the blood circulation, the bacteria can soon spread into the system and the client becomes infected. So a completely sterile needle is essential and will hopefully become law, enforced for public protection. Electrologists are not the only people who have to be aware of these problems.

They concern anyone who uses needles that do or could pierce the skin — acupuncture treatments, ear piercing, tattooing, etc. Medical staff have long ago gained the advantages of sterilization by gamma irradiation for their hypodermics, and many other sterile dressings, and now this completely foolproof method of disposable needles with guaranteed sterility is available to electrologists. The United Kingdom leads the world at present with this new technology.

The fact that electrology is often performed outside of a professional clinic practice, in association with beauty therapy, perhaps in a store complex (a clinic within the store or a concession arrangement) means that sterilization is more difficult to control, and the working situation is more open to increased risk. However, if some basic but effective procedures are taken, there is no reason why standards should drop. It just requires a careful approach on the part of the operator.

Very simple procedures are all that are needed for the basic hygiene of tools, cleanliness of the working environment, and correct sterility of the epilation needles. If these procedures are adhered to, then they should be enough to combat all existing diseases that might assail the electrologist in her work. Viral diseases such as hepatitis B (being carried through blood transference) are the greatest danger to the profession, as individuals can be carriers and be quite unaware they have a problem. Hepatitis B has highlighted the problem, as sterilization methods which were once though adequate will not kill the virus. The industry has responded with information, medical help from the best qualified staff, and action from the manufacturers. The results are gamma irradiated needles which are disposable; sterilization methods which are based on heat in a form able to kill the micro-organisms concerned; and a new look at chemical methods to see where they can be useful in the chain of hygiene that makes up a correct working situation for electrology. These procedures are being confirmed by registration, and promoted through a free interchange of knowledge between the medical and electrology professions.

STERILIZATION — WHAT DOES IT MEAN?

Essentially it means the irreversible destruction or injury of all living micro-organisms, including bacteria, fungi, and viruses. This means making an article germ-free, by destroying all kinds of bacteria present — whether harmful or beneficial. Unfortunately, different methods are needed to kill all the different forms of bacteria. For example, sterilization by heat at a temperature of 100°C (212°F), which is the boiling point of water, kills some organisms, but organisms such as spore-forming bacteria

and viruses require higher temperatures. To destroy these organisms, boiling will not suffice and an autoclave sterilizer (steam under pressure, like a pressure cooker), or a hot oven is needed. Both methods have the capacity to reach and maintain the higher temperatures needed for viruses such as hepatitis B.

Hospitals, dentists, and training centres all use these systems satisfactorily and have surgical tools, etc., in the sterilization process for 30 to 40 minutes before being ready to use. Sterilization by heat requires the temperature to be maintained long enough for the heat to penetrate through the entire substance that is being sterilized — and items must be very clean before being sterilized, all skin fragments and blood being carefully removed, especially if they have become baked on to the needles through the epilation process. Heat must be constantly left on, not switched on and off at random, otherwise sterilization would be unreliable and not have time to penetrate and kill all the organisms present. So a rigorous system must be followed, if there is to be no margin of error or risk in the procedure. An automatically timed autoclave is a large investment for a small clinic, and perhaps not the most practical solution. In the training situation, however, it is a godsend, ensuring sterile tools are always available, and any problems of cross-infection which can occur in a busy clinic are easily prevented. Tools need lifting out from the upper chamber with forceps (being very hot) just prior to use, ensuring the chamber temperature is below 80°C, and the autoclave is not still under pressure.

It is wise to remember that the process can blunt the tools' keen edges, so a little more attention to maintenance might be needed. It is wise to consider electrology as a tiny surgical task where the risks of cross-infection are high, and therefore take proper precautions. Sterilizing existing needles (if the disposable sterile-packed ones are not available) and tweezers can be achieved using the hot bead-type of sterilizer. This is designed specially for the task, and copes well with the area of greatest risk, leaving the rest of clinic sterilization to be organized by more general methods, such as chemical vapour methods in closed cabinets.

STERILE NEEDLES — THE PRESENT LAW

Gamma irradiated, sterile, disposable needles, individually packed, are the obvious answer to the problems of providing a truly sterile needle every time. They leave no margin of risk from incomplete sterilization methods and most importantly, provide a brand new, perfect needle to use. The fact that the client receives a new needle which is completely sterile is a strong selling point showing the care taken for the client, and the service should be promoted this way. These disposable needles are an advancement that cannot be

ignored, a fact which must be supported as the best thing that has happened to the industry's standards in years; these forward-thinking procedures deserve the industry's encouragement. It is necessary to progress in technology if the field is to move forward professionally, and gain more public support and consumer confidence.

The small additional cost of the needle should be added to the fee, and once the needle has been used on the client for her treatment it is thrown away like a disposable hypodermic syringe, into what is known as a 'sharps' box, ready for final disposal. Despite the enormous costs of setting up an automated gamma irradiation system for providing the individually packed Ferrie needles, the actual cost of a needle to the electrologist is relatively small. The cost of the sterile needles will drop even further if they become the automatic choice for every professional operator, as volume turnover always helps reduce production costs. So the more professionals that change to the sterile needle method, the more they will ensure cheaper prices and greater availability internationally.

The local authorities' position on needle sterility, guided by the Public Health Laboratory Service Communicable Disease Surveillance Centre, is that gamma irradiated needles are the most suitable and the most foolproof method of ensuring sterility; other than that, the hot bead method, completed correctly with the needle in the heating chamber for one minute, and the autoclave method, 152°C (305°F) for 3 minutes, are also satisfactory methods. There is an official publication written by Dr Noah, *A Guide to Hygienic Skin Piercing* (available from the Public Health Service) which states the problem and its solutions exactly to the Public Health Service requirements, and this will be used as the guidelines by all local authorities when registering the clinics and operators who offer the service. It is extremely beneficial to have medical support in the fight against contagious diseases, and to have the different systems of sterilization put through a series of medical trials so that everyone can know their effects and advantages in the work. It is useless relying on a system that leaves the clinic practice with less than perfect protection against these serious diseases. The industry can turn a blind eye or kid itself no longer; the law forces a responsible attitude.

Some sterilization systems are not easy to apply in the small clinic environment, although they undoubtedly work extremely well. Others have their shortcomings and cannot provide 100% reliability every time, which leaves a critical margin for error. Systems can be made to work well in laboratory conditions, but are hit and miss in the clinic with the human element involved in the procedures required. Questions like, 'How strong is the sterilizing fluid?' 'Is it old and has it lost its power?' 'How long does the needle

stay in the hot bead?' 'How long have tools been in the autoclave?' All these questions have to be asked and checked. Are articles clean when they go into the chemical vapour cabinet? If not they will not be sterilized effectively.

Understanding the whole procedure is not difficult, and really comes down to keeping a clean clinic, using disinfectants for background control of bacteria, and moving on to specialized sterilization methods for tools and needles, the highest risk area.

GETTING IN LINE WITH STERILIZATION

To meet the Public Health Service requirements coming into force, certain points must be covered. The local authority will use as its guidelines the work done by Dr Noah and the Communicable Disease Surveillance Centre, where certain equipment for sterilization has been tested to assess its performance. Keeping a clean clinic, and taking special care over needle sterility is required, and licensing permission will only be given if the correct system is seen to be in action. Once the facts are known then the correct equipment can be purchased; do not expect the manufacturers to teach the basics of sterilization — they are there to provide the means, not the knowledge. Electrologists must gain the knowledge themselves.

It is the electrologist's responsibility to know how far her clinic follows the law, and to make any changes needed to come into line. These tightening up procedures are for the protection of public health, to safeguard the operator in her professional work, and to avoid unethical individuals being in business and putting people at risk. So do not resent the new requirements, just get into line and then you will feel secure. Consumer confidence will build up in the process, with direct effects on business turnover.

BACKGROUND TO CLINIC STERILIZATION AND SANITATION

Sterilization means making an object germ-free by destroying all kinds of bacteria, whether harmful or beneficial. It means the irreversible injury or destruction of all living micro-organisms, including bacteria, fungi, and viruses (it has been seen that different methods are needed to destroy all the bacterial enemies of the electrologist — so a simple solution is needed).

Antiseptics retard or kill bacteria and can be used in a variety of ways, in different dilutions (proportions of water to antiseptic solution or substances) to clean surfaces, tools, sponges, brushes, forceps, etc.

Disinfection is a general term for any process which disinfects or decontaminates an object or area of the body by destroying bacteria or micro-organisms. The terms germicide and bactericide are also used.

Sanitization is a cleansing procedure which causes temporary destruction of bacteria on objects. It is a rather out-dated method but one which can still provide the basis of achieving a hygienic environment.

CHEMICAL STERILIZING AGENTS

The roles of antiseptics and disinfectants differ in that many antiseptics only retard bacterial growth, while for adequate sterility a more intense or concentrated solution, such as a disinfectant, should be used. So the strength of the chemical agent used is an essential factor — and both antiseptics and disinfectants play a useful role. One does not eliminate the need for the other, especially as disinfectants are often poisonous and pungent in odour and are not suitable for general purposes, surface cleansing, etc. Disinfectants can also have a harsh bleaching action which can be corrosive to instruments; they have to be powerful to do their task of bacterial destruction really well. So both need to be used with care, otherwise they can affect the health of the people working with them. Use disinfectants with restraint, and only when really needed; back them up with more acceptable and pleasant antiseptic and cleansing measures. The hygiene chain of events always needs basic cleansing to come first in the sequence; this allows overall sterilization to be more effective and more easily achieved. Sound basic hygiene limits the need for harsh methods of sterilization.

There are some useful and effective chemical agents available on the market. One used widely around the world is a quaternary ammonium compound (QACS or QUATS) which is available under the brand name of Zephiran Chloride in the United States, and is also the active chemical agent behind Cetavlon in the United Kingdom. Made up as a diluted solution, ready to use, it is also available as QUATS in the United States, and is widely used in electrology for different tasks according to the dilution prepared (proportion of chemical agent to distilled water). It is active against bacteria, some viruses, fungi and protozoa, but bacterial spores are resistant. The usual proportions that are readily available are a 1:1750 solution. If made up within the clinic from a more concentrated solution, only distilled water must be used and it has to be fresh (not itself contaminated in any way). Tap water containing metallic ions and organic matter can alter the solution and can reduce antibacterial potency. Resin deionized water should not be used since it may contain pathogenic bacteria. It is

easiest overall to ask the pharmacist to make up a solution, or buy it ready-made. If unavailable, find a simple way of getting the correct proportions — buy a simple liquid measure and make up the amount needed for a short period. It is not complicated, but must be done accurately — one of the routine tasks of the clinic.

The QUATS solutions such as Zephiran Chloride and Cetavlon are made inactive by soaps and anionic detergents. So follow the correct sequence of events — cleanse and rinse, and then sterilize where extra protection is needed. Remember that antiseptics do not achieve sterilization though they have a most important role, *they do not destroy bacterial spores and certain viruses — including the etiologic agent of infectious hepatitis.*

Formaldehyde can be used in a number of ways in the sterilizing procedures in electrology, and works by creating a vapour when the solution is activated by heat (such as the small heat generated by a low-wattage light bulb). It can also be used in a strong concentration to sterilize tools so long as the tools are immersed in the solution. It is always pungent and will make the eyes water, so is always used within a closed cabinet which is only opened to remove the items as needed.

Formaldehyde can be used in a 5 to 10% solution within a closed sterilizing cabinet to sterilize a variety of tools and applicators. This is the most popular method internationally, and when linked with the use of disposable sterile needles or a hot bead needle sterilizer (since the chemical vapour method cannot ensure needle sterility) provides a complete sterilization system for electrology. It works by the application of a small quantity of the formaldehyde solution (5% is acceptable, but 10% more effective as far as use in the clinic is concerned) to the sponge placed in the small tray at the back or bottom of the closed cabinet. The heat from the small bulb which illuminates the cabinet, activates and vaporizes the solution on the sponge, and this affects the entire cabinet and its contents. The cabinet must stay closed and have a well-fitting door or lid, and the items to be sterilized must be kept in the cabinet for a minimum of 20 minutes from the moment when the cabinet becomes warm. No power as such is used in the sterilization process, just a gentle heat to vaporize and activate the chemical agent. Large capacity sterilizers allow space for small tools, sponges, beauty therapy items, etc., to receive effective sterilization if they are placed in the cabinet really clean to begin with. This form of chemical sterilizing is a safe and popular system for the busy clinic, as formaldehyde solution is readily available from chemists and equipment manufacturers, and the method is cheap, easy to use and effective. Electrologists must remember to top up the sponge within the cabinet with the solution, and be guided by its pungency when in action. Avoid taking deep breaths of the solution or handling it, as it is a caustic agent and harmful in

its concentrated form; any solution that gets on the skin must be rinsed away immediately. A 5 or 10% solution can also be used to immerse tools directly, such as tweezers, and then these can be stored in the sterile cabinet until needed. Once the initial 20 to 30 minutes of vaporizing has taken place, the cabinet can be switched off and just used as a sterile storage cabinet, but it must be remembered that in a busy clinic where the lid or door is constantly being opened and shut, the items will lose their sterility, and therefore the cabinet may need to stay in action at all times. The method of application depends on the use the equipment gets within the clinic practice.

PHYSICAL STERILIZATION AGENTS — NON CHEMICAL METHODS OF STERILIZATION

Boiling water — tools, etc., submerged in boiling water (100°C/212°F) for 20 minutes.
Dry heat — 171°C/340°F for 60 minutes, in special heating cabinets/ovens.
Glass beads — 232°C/450°F for 10 seconds minimum. (United Kingdom regulations stipulate up to one minute for complete protection.)
Autoclaving — tools, etc., kept in saturated steam under pressure, at 15 p.s.i. (pounds per square inch) 121°C/250°F for 15 minutes and 32 p.s.i., 152°C/305°F for 3 minutes.

Exposure to ultraviolet rays is sometimes suggested, and does have its uses in hairdressing where mainly hard plastic tools like combs, etc., are in use. It does present a problem for electrologists because the instruments are only affected on the surface they present to the UV rays, so the underneath side does not receive any rays and cannot therefore be sterilized. This method is appropriate, however, where the need for complete sterility is not so critical — but it does not meet the exacting standards set for electrology.

Many systems aim to sterilize, some are convenient to use, others not, but all can be used effectively to some degree. Unfortunately no one system suits all circumstances, but if the basic way they work is understood, then a good choice can be made.

HOW THE DIFFERENT METHODS OF STERILIZATION WORK

Water can produce the highest temperatures most readily for sterilization purposes, especially under pressure (like a pressure cooker) — the autoclave being an example. Boiling water,

however, can only reach 100 °C (212 °F) — not high enough for resistant viral strains like hepatitis B. So the water temperature has to be forced up under pressure to 171 °C (340 °F) minimum, and objects must stay at this temperature for 30 minutes (or even longer for complete sterility to be assured. So it is no use setting the autoclave at 149°C (300 °F), and believing this will suffice, because certain resistant bacterial spores and viral strains will not be destroyed by the action.

Hot air methods (cabinets/ovens/hot beads) do not get to the required temperatures as easily or as quickly as fluids. Dry heat cabinets and ovens can get to 171 °C (340 °F), but need 60 minutes to produce the desired level of sterilization. They can do the job very well, and if large objects are being sterilized such as in a medical situation, the method still has many uses, but enough time must be given to the procedure. Many objects, such as plastics, cannot stand the high temperature and naturally any metal object going through the process will be placed under strain which in time could lead to metal fatigue and possible fracture. The heating process must not be interrupted, and the heat level must be maintained throughout.

The hot oven provides a large area and is relatively slow to reach the required temperature to do the job. Hot bead sterilizers use the hot air principle, but contain and concentrate the heat into a small area, distributing the heat through tiny glass beads (the smaller the better) so that a very high temperature is maintained. The hot bead method has the same effect as a very large oven but sterilization occurs over a tiny area and in a very short space of time, 30 seconds to several minutes, depending on the equipment used and local authorities' rulings in force in the area of work. So, it is still a hot air method, especially worked out to give excellent results for needles and forceps (tweezers), etc. Naturally a strain is placed on the needles from this form of heat concentration, and they must be closely inspected for signs of metal fatigue, possible fracture, blunting and any other damage. No precision needle can go through this procedure many times before it must be discarded, especially as it also has to cope with the strain of the high-frequency short wave diathermy epilation current during electrology treatment. Insulated needles with their protective outer coating up most of the needle, cannot really stand this form of sterilization, as the coating fragments and makes a less than perfect tip to work with. For sterilizing insulated needles, chemical methods must be employed, to ensure protection against resistant viral strains. Future progress may make it possible for insulated needles to become gamma irradiated just as the Ferrie needles are now, and available in the same presentation — sterile-packed and disposable.

Hot bead sterilizers build up enough heat around the instruments

(needles) to cause a rapid destruction of bacteria without undue damage to the metal items themselves. Different models are available and some have been tested by the health authorities and are seen to give varied results — so it is wise to ask if the equipment to be purchased has gained Public Health Authority recognition.

The hot bead sterilizers in the United States come under the scrutiny of the FDA (Food and Drug Administration), and have to meet standards of manufacture and performance. The FDA controls and checks the device but like the United Kingdom health authorities does not 'approve' any particular model, it gives the tests' results and findings, makes recommendations, and can prevent a model being sold or restrict its use to specified personnel if it is felt that a need exists to protect the public. For example, if an epilation machine or hot bead sterilizer is found to be unsafe, either to use or in the task it is supposed to perform, then its manufacture could be stopped, or its distribution halted under the Protection of Public Safety at Work. If the FDA feels, given enough evidence, that the use of epilation machines should be restricted to trained staff working directly under the control and guidance of medical staff, then it could restrict the use of the machines in this way. Evidence of malpractice, spread of infectious diseases through careless work, etc., could all make these restrictions enforceable. Health departments involved with the control of infectious diseases can naturally have tremendous influence, and could bring about radical changes in how an industry can function, and perform its work. As a result, it may soon be obligatory internationally for operators to use disposable sterile needles, such as 'ONE-TIME' or 'STEREX' brands.

Wherever an opportunity for human error exists, such as with hot bead sterilizers, the operator must take especial care to follow the procedures carefully. The needles must be clean and free from skin debris, blood, etc., before being treated. They should be sterilized just prior to use, not long before, and time taken to see that they are correctly placed in the heating chamber, and kept in long enough. In the United Kingdom the 1 to 10 minutes suggested (depending on the hot bead model used) seems excessive but undoubtedly is suggested to ensure the needles do receive enough time to be fully sterile. The hot bead method is accepted in the United Kingdom, but disposable sterile needles will always gain greater medical approval as they alone leave no possibility of loss of sterility due to human error, or carelessness.

Chemical disinfectants follow a different path, and for general purposes are extremely useful, and have stood the beauty and electrology industry in good stead for many years. The use of chemical vapour cabinets, wall-mounted and free-standing, or built into special storage systems like the *Beauty Gallery,* form an important part of general clinic hygiene. They provide an easy way

of keeping equipment sterile and cope with most forms of bacteria likely to assail the professional electrologist or therapist. Now with a greater range of micro-organisms recognized as being hazards to professional practice, they are not totally sufficient, but still have an important and major role in the actual sanitization chain of hygiene.

For the sterilization of small tools, viscose sponges, brushes, cotton wool, forceps (tweezers), plastic cups, sponge envelopes, glass electrodes, etc., chemical vapour methods form a gentle way of sterilizing those objects which are likely to be used on a client. The system has been seen to work very well if the cabinet is kept shut for the 20 to 30 minutes needed, and so should be organized at a quiet time such as lunchtime or at the start of the day; in this way the procedure is not disrupted by a new object being placed inside the cabinet half-way through the time needed. Make sure sufficient space is available around the items to be sterilized, because the chemical vapour cannot work if the cabinet is over-full, and if areas to be sterilized cannot be reached by the vapour produced. Formaldehyde is very volatile, so keep the cabinet closed and do not allow the fumes to drift into the clinic atmosphere. Store the active solution in a cool place, and never have it close to any direct source of heat — remember it is an active chemical, treat it with caution.

SKIN CLEANSING PRIOR TO EPILATION TREATMENT

There are many schools of thought on cleansing and preparing the skin prior to epilation. Some professionals use Zephiran Chloride (based on quaternary ammonium compounds) while others prefer a 70% alcohol solution. Cetavlon is popular in the United Kingdom, as are more natural solutions based on soothing and anti-inflammatory elements like tincture of benzoin and elder-flower water. It should be remembered that the skin is excellent at healing itself, and it sometimes benefits from being allowed to heal naturally. Removing all natural micro-organisms from its surface prior to epilation can be a disruption of the normal skin recovery processes. What is important is not to introduce any unwanted bacteria into the skin, either before, during, or after the treatment, so careful cleansing to remove make-up is vital, as is home-care advice to the client to avoid the risks of infection. Electrologists do need a wetting agent to work with, and soothing preparations to calm the skin as they work, but alcohol has the action of closing the pores which makes probing difficult, so would not seem an ideal choice. Harsh chemicals should really be avoided, they are best kept for sterilizing the tools not the skin.

After-care items can be based on calming elements such as camomile, calamine, azulene, etc., just making sure the client is not sensitive to these elements. Calamine cream is available in many formulations and provides a cover to protect the skin area treated, and settles the surface capillaries initially after epilation. Every electrologist has her own favourite, and many use only one lotion for cleansing after make-up removal, for padding and soothing as they work, and for soothing the area after treatment is concluded.

HEPATITIS, HERPES, AND ACQUIRED IMMUNE DEFICIENCY SYNDROME (AIDS) — THE PRESENT POSITION

How has all the anxiety about hepatitis B come about, what is the story, and why is it causing such a lot of changes to professional therapy? It is useful to consider the circumstances leading up to the present changes, as although the actual case which highlighted the problems did not derive from electrology treatment, it is a problem that could happen in electrology extremely easily.

Acupuncture needles obviously pierce the skin, as do the needles used for tattooing and ear-piercing, and many people consider that electrology needles do not. But a viral infection being carried in blood tissue, from an infected individual or carrier, *can* be passed on by the electrology needle very easily. This is because viral micro-organisms are extremely difficult to kill, and normal sterilization methods, even when scrupulously carried out, cannot kill the viral strain of hepatitis B. As we have seen, special methods are required, and even these leave the possibility of error. So it was not that sterilization was not carried out, it was possibly just not effective against the problem encountered.

Electrology, despite every precaution, provides a risk situation when hepatitis B is considered. Blood, skin debris, etc., from an infected individual might be carried on the needle and pass on to another person — unless the needle is disposable and thrown away after use. Even when a needle has been carefully cleaned, inspected, and sterilized by the approved methods, the virulent micro-organism could still be active. So unless disposable needles are used, the risk of passing on hepatitis B is always present, as the client may be suffering from the condition and not know it, or may be a carrier (that is can pass the disease but does not actually suffer from the symptoms herself).

Blood carrying the virus may be removed from the needle by cleansing, but the strong viral micro-organisms will not be affected by chemical sterilization (chemical vapour methods) or by heat

methods unless perfectly performed. The methods internationally accepted for this special problem are

(1) disposable sterile needles, gamma irradiated and individually packed.
(2) hot bead sterilizers accepted by local authorities to the guidelines set out in the United Kingdom by the Public Health Service Communicable Disease Surveillance Centre, and confirmed by Dr Noah in his publication: *A Guide to Hygienic Skin Piercing* (available from the Public Health Service).
(3) autoclave sterilizing — 30 minutes at a minimum of 171°C (340°F).
(4) phenol (chemical method with immersion) 5% solution for 30 minutes. This method is accepted in the United States. Phenol is a poison which must be used with extreme care, but which provides a means of sterilizing insulated needles which cannot stand the hot bead process, and are not yet available in a disposable gamma sterilized form, mainly because of their high cost of production.

The three problems of viral hepatitis, herpes, and Acquired Immune Deficiency Syndrome (AIDS) are receiving a great deal of media exposure around the world, as they are very serious diseases which in some cases can result in death to the sufferer. So it is worth our while to know about them and to know that we are doing our best to protect ourselves and our clients against their spread through our work.

VIRAL HEPATITIS

Viral hepatitis is in fact three distinct diseases caused by different agents: hepatitis A virus (HAV), hepatitis B virus (HBV), and non-A and non-B virus (NANBV).

Infectious hepatitis, or hepatitis A, is caused by an RNA viral agent, spread primarily by the faecal oral route. It is found in the faeces (human excreta/waste) during the last 2 weeks of its incubation period. Once the person actually shows themselves to have jaundice, the faeces are basically non infectious. So before the individuals are aware of their problem, they have been incubating the condition and can have passed it to others, through careless personal hygiene, failure to wash hands after going to the toilet, etc. Hepatitis A survives well in humans, because the infected individuals show no sign of symptoms during the stage at which they are most infectious to others — the incubation stage. During this time the virus is readily transmitted to others, as it is very difficult to control, and any small oversights in food preparation from an infected individual can result in a severe problem occurring. In fact outbreaks are usually related to the contamina-

tion of food or water which has become infected with diseased human faeces. Individuals involved in the food industry have to be scrupulously careful, and constant hygiene checks from the health authorities regulate the preparation of processed food very vigilantly. Hepatitis A and typhoid are often the first signs that water is contaminated by human waste, and in primitive conditions, or after a disaster, an unclean water supply is a major problem in maintaining the health of the community.

The hepatitis A virus does not cause a chronic condition, and individuals who have had the disease once seem immune from it for the rest of their lives. It is not thought that individuals are carriers of hepatitis A, it is only at the active incubatory stage that it can affect others through the faecal route or through careless habits.

Hepatitis B, or serum hepatitis, is caused by a DNA virus which differs from other known viruses and is a prototype of a new class or type of viral agent. Hepatitis B has been detected in blood, saliva, and other body fluids for several weeks or months before, during and after the symptomatic stage of the disease (stage where the individual is showing signs or symptoms of the disease and is actually ill). A percentage of those individuals, 5 to 10%, may become carriers of the disease, that is free from signs of it, but capable of infecting another person (especially through the blood — such as blood transmitted on a needle point). The incubation period of hepatitis B is usually about 3 months, but can be longer, up to 6 months, and the person is very infectious for most of that time.

There also appear to be individuals in the community who although they have never actually had hepatitis B are carriers. These people are a great risk to the professional electrologist, as they would not necessarily show a contra-indication to treatment like clients with a history of the condition. High-risk groups are identified as drug abusers, male homosexuals, patients on renal dialysis, etc. — individuals who for one reason or another have placed additional strains on their bodies' defence mechanisms, or ability to fight infection, either from natural physical defects or physical abuses to their systems. HBV contracted in the final months of pregnancy can result in the child born becoming a carrier of the disease, having acquired the virus from its mother's blood supply.

HERPES SIMPLEX VIRUS

Herpes simplex virus (HSV) is a viral disease which is transmitted by direct contact, that is skin to skin. There are various areas which it can attack: for example, lesions may be found on the face, mouth and nose areas (called cold sores) and inside the mouth (known as oral herpes), etc. HSV can spread between people or around the

individual themselves. The different forms of HSV can be spread through kissing, sexual intercourse and saliva contaminations of contact lenses. Even infants can be infected if the mother has genital herpes and the baby is delivered in the normal way through the birth passage.

All individuals who come into close contact with people in the course of their work are at risk from herpes. Contact with active lesions brings a risk of infection, so doctors, nurses, medical health workers and electrologists have to take precautions at all times and be vigilant about skin inspection, careful counselling and clients' records. The virus enters through a break in the skin, or through mucus membranes, such as the linings around openings in the body, the vagina, nose, mouth, etc. It then seeks out the nervous system closest to its point of entry or site of infection. Once established in the nerve cell the virus stays in that same area, and does not spread into the bloodstream or move on further into the body.

HSV may remain dormant in the body for long periods, or become active then heal and appear to be gone only to reappear periodically. The pattern of dormancy and reoccurrence makes this condition a real risk to the electrologist, and she must take precautions in her work to avoid contracting the condition herself. Good personal health and scrupulous attention to hygiene — personal and in the clinic — are the first steps to a defence against the condition. Checking the client's medical history carefully is also vital, as then additional precautions can be put into action, or the client tactfully declined or postponed.

There does not seem to be any way a person can build up resistance to these viruses. Dormant viruses are believed to be activated by certain factors which precipitate an attack, such as sun burn, exposure to sunlight, extreme cold, local injury or trauma, respiratory infections (coughs, colds, etc.) and hormone changes preceding menstruation.

Herpes has an incubatory period of 2 to 7 days, and then a fluid-filled blister (vesicule) erupts, followed by a shallow ulceration. Self-healing follows, and as the ulcer forms a crust it heals underneath. Cold sores are some of the most annoying skin irritations known, which spread very fast, and cause real misery. The lesion usually remains active for 7 to 21 days, but several lesions may have developed, and as one heals, another is going through its active phase. Moist skin lesions heal much slower than dry ones.

Herpes is infectious at every stage, so electrologists must be aware of the problem, and learn not only to recognize it, but how to avoid spreading it further on the client or contracting it herself. If the way the disease progresses is understood, then it is possible that

the problem can be discussed rationally and sympathetically with the client to work out a solution even if this means postponing treatment.

Herpes can occur in anyone, regular clients, new ones, etc., but is most frequent among people who spend the summer overdoing the sun tan, without lip protection in high ultraviolet areas — countries like Australia and South Africa, and people who spend time in Europe during the bitterly cold winters. If a client turns up for her regular treatment with a small cold sore in a dry stage on the upper lip, it is stupid to cause embarrassment to her, but certainly that area cannot be treated. With care, and use of ultra-light surgical gloves, another area such as the chin or eyebrows could be treated. A quiet consultation explains the reasons to the client, but does not lose a valuable client to the business. Do not take the risk of accidental contact, wear gloves, or keep completely away from the face and treat an entirely different area.

If the lesion is active and open, causing distress, the client should not be treated at all, and advised to postpone treatment until the area is clear. If the client has lesions in her mouth or near her eyes, advice to see a doctor is the correct procedure. Self-remedies, such as creams, ointments, spirit-based lotions, or concealing make-up, should be advised against as these will all interfere and slow the healing process. If the client has recently undergone surgery and yet has no history of lesions, or any present, it may still be important to take care, as she may have a high potential for HSV, and contact with her saliva could pass the infection on to the electrologist's fingers as she works near the mouth. This is because the client may be on immunosuppressing drugs, following a surgical transplant (kidney transplant, etc.). Clients undergoing chemotherapy and/or radiation therapy for cancer are another group to take special care with. All these clients require medical permission to treat, and may benefit from the use of antibiotic cream following each treatment (prescribed by their own doctor) to help the body fight infection.

ACQUIRED IMMUNE DEFICIENCY SYNDROME (AIDS)

AIDS has come from obscurity to be a world-wide problem in recent years, and now its path and victims can be traced. In the United States doctors in 33 states have reported hundreds of cases with many fatalities. The problem can affect both men and women, but is prevalent among homosexual males. The actual cause of the syndrome is still unknown; this makes it a problem of concern to everybody, especially those like electrologists, who work closely with people and do not themselves have the protection of working under direct medical supervision. Clients can come in for treatment from all walks of life, there is no medical vetting as a safeguard.

The most likely causes of AIDS are getting clearer, under intense medical investigation on an international level. The victims suffer from a decreased ability to resist infections and fall victim to a host of problems. Their ability to resist infection is deficient, and they can die a very slow and painful death. The cause of AIDS may be due to a mutant micro-organism such as a virus, or a combination of infectious, immunological, social and environmental factors. As the disease seems to be closely linked with the intimate contact between homosexuals, one might wonder why this problem should be so worrying to electrologists, who probably seldom come into contact with them. The truth is that while the real facts behind AIDS are not fully known, a very serious risk does exist, and because the disease is connected with a reduced resistance to disease others could become involved with the condition.

Certainly so far it has been found most common among homosexuals, especially it is thought, those who are promiscuous and have many sexual partners, and the risk is heightened by the use of stimulant drugs within the sexual act. These possibly having an immunosuppressive effect on the body's system.

City living seems to bring the problem to the foreground possibly because of the greater concentrations of homosexuals in these large population areas, where unusual life styles seldom attract as much attention. What has to be considered is that some homosexuals do also have heterosexual inclinations, and their female partners may in time succumb to the same pressures on their immune defence systems. As so little is known about the condition in real terms, and with homosexuals being such a large and growing part of society, working in every walk of life, it is impossible to ignore the seriousness of the problem. Perhaps their sexual inclinations place them most or first at risk as they subject their bodies to greater physical strain than heterosexual people, but it could become a general problem if its cause is not discovered. The risks of the disease being spread through blood transfusions has been highlighted in recent times. Blood donors, unaware they are already suffering from AIDS have donated blood to be used within the medical blood bank system. Now, homosexuals are being asked not to give blood because of the danger of this blood being contaminated and spreading the disease to others.

11

Being successful in the business

GETTING STARTED

Once qualified, the graduate will find that she has several options: she can either become self-employed, or she can work as an employee in a store clinic or beauty salon, or she can work in a partnership with an established practitioner.

Going it alone is a big step, especially if funds are not readily available for loans and current interest rates are high. Rents are high, and equipment is costly. There are also telephone installation charges plus business and advertising expenses to find, which eat into initial funds.

A deciding factor with regards to location might be whether one is single or married and how much potential business is in the area. Can the population of the area provide a living for another electrologist? Perhaps moving into a new community will provide better opportunities and a better living. If one has trained with a tutor, it is sometimes better to move away and start a business in a new area to avoid over-saturation of the market, especially if the local population is small.

WORKING FOR SOMEBODY ELSE/ SELF-EMPLOYED OR EMPLOYEE

Graduates of electrology often make their first income by working for the people who taught them, either as an assistant, or working self-employed by renting space in the same practice. This is useful in several ways: the established practitioner gets help from someone who has trained in her methods, and the graduate gains the time to acquire business experience, while her confidence and skills grow. The situation can have drawbacks for both sides, as often the employer will find their new helper moving on to private practice as soon as they can afford it. It is a cause for conflict, and not a very satisfactory arrangement for the employer, who must then start all over again; but it is understandable, as everyone

wants to fulfil personal ambitions. A good honest discussion at the start could save a lot of ill-feeling later, if the employee is young and likely to move on, then this is a risk that has to be faced, honestly and out in the open. The employer must be prepared, and not feel put out when the inevitable happens. If the employee is mature, and perhaps not quite so ambitious, or may even just prefer working for someone else, then this can be ideal and may lead to a partnership at a later date which would secure the situation on both sides. A partnership might not necessarily be the answer, but some scheme or form of incentive is needed to make the employee feel valued and secure.

WORKING RIGHTS

It is up to electrologists to find out about ways of working and what their rights are. Schools and colleges can give the lead by making students aware of both sides of the picture — employer and employee. Where there are no minimum wage scales or official ways to regulate earnings, or fixed treatment charges, the right rate for the job can vary considerably. Knowing about the costs of the overheads of running a business — both seen and unseen costs — will give the newly qualified operator a more accurate idea of what her employer has to pay out before any profits are made. It will also offer valuable guidance should the question of running a personal business, and becoming self-employed, ever come up. The information needed covers many facets, but can be looked at briefly in terms of capital expenditure, fixed costs, expenses, insurance, advertising, etc.

Working for someone else means that an employment contract is required, and this should state the minimum guaranteed wage, commissions if paid, etc. It is often the case that the newcomer is expected to build her own clientele and has to manage on 50% of professional fees taken. This can be extremely difficult, and a guaranteed wage, even a low one, or 50% of the fees taken, whichever is higher, would be a fairer thing to ask for. It is in everyone's interest to know the individual can survive financially and it still provides good incentives to the individual to develop her own clientele.

Some employment contracts provide protection for the owner in the event that the employee decides to leave and go into her own practice, perhaps close by. It attempts to ensure that the owner's practice will be left intact, especially as quite considerable amounts of time and money have probably been spent promoting the new operator in the practice. Therefore employers feel it is important to have a radius clause in the contract, which specifies the distance a new practice must relocate to, for example, 5 to 10 miles if in a country location or small town situation. In a city

this radius clause is hard to enforce, and is perhaps not even fair to demand; it rather depends on population figures.

Building up new business in a practice is normally accomplished both by dealing with the overflow from the employer, or existing staff, and by taking new business as it is achieved through advertising (*Yellow Pages,* newspaper advertisements, public relations work, etc.).

It is unrealistic to think that an employee will be forever content to work for someone else, and if this natural transition can be dealt with professionally and realistically, then no ill-feelings occur which could harm the business.

RENTING YOUR SPACE

Whether an employee or employer, you need to know what is a fair rent, so look at commercial office rates per square metre or foot; this will show what is available for the money. Ask the advice of your colleagues, they will help, especially if the business planned is a good distance from their own! Do not pay enormous rentals for space until the business turnover has built up; it could mean a constant worry about making out. Start small and do the work well, and aim to make some money in the pocket rather than just pay the overheads.

If the offer of space in association with another business or medical practice comes up, compare the cost of the space and its advantages to other space for rent before making commitments. Avoid being taken for a ride by unscrupulous landlords. Keep looking for space that is in the right price range, in the correct area, bright and cheerful in outlook and that people can get to fairly easily. Do not be afraid to go and look at unusual space to rent: a commercial setting is not always a disadvantage, people close by offer a ready clientele, convenient and close to their work. Office space is not the only kind available, and in association with a shopping precinct, a mall or secondary trading centre, a business can be equally successful if sufficient advertising in the *Yellow Pages* and local papers is done. It is important then to promote yourself and your skills well.

Renting an office in which to practise is the first step. Check that all the correct legal steps are taken to ensure that electrology is allowed to be practised in that space. Do not sign contracts until this point is checked. If a change of use from office to clinic is needed, do not take a risk — wait until your planning application is successful. Do not sign for space or pay a deposit for space not yet available. Go somewhere else, use your money on equipment, get moving and build your practice. You can always move on to a better venue later. Your skill will hold your clients for you.

Do take care that you have a proper lease and will not have to move at a moment's notice. Get a proper agreement signed, even if it is only for a 6 month period, with an option for longer. You are the customer, buying the space for a time; therefore make the ground rules to suit you, not the landlord. It is not always easy to find what you want, but it is well worth a little effort.

LEGAL REQUIREMENTS

It is necessary to pay attention to matters of insurance, Department of Health regulations, licensing and registration rules in force in your country or county. Licensing ensures that the client receives treatment from a qualified operator, who has undergone a set period of training and works to good standards of practice and hygiene. It protects the consumer and indirectly the profession from the unqualified, unscrupulous operator. These measures have been set up to protect the client from malpractice and to protect the industry from the effects of untrained or unethical individuals setting up business and offering treatment. Professional indemnity insurance is normally available to qualified operators, through their associations, and public liability insurance is also needed if the work is completed in a private practice, clinic or home practice situation. This is in case a client is injured on the commercial premises, and claims against the business. Make sure that all the insurance needs are covered: a policy for loss of earnings through injury or illness is an excellent security for the busy operator. Usually available for a very small cash outlay, yet so useful if unexpected events curtail or halve your business activities for a few weeks or months, it provides a weekly figure to compensate for loss of income from the work.

CHOOSING EQUIPMENT

After finding a place to practise comes the critical task of choosing equipment. Choose wisely as the equipment will be in use for a long time; get the best available. If you have trained on only one make of epilation machine, at least find out about the others, what they offer, compare prices and advantages. Read the trade magazines, join associations, go to meetings and conferences, see what is about in the market place. Ask discerning questions — reputable manufacturers will be pleased to help you and get you underway. Do take time picking your chair/couch and stool, epilation unit and magnifier. Even if you feel that you have trained on the very best available, take the time to check out the alternatives then reject them if you want to. Remember that a school or college may have been equipped many years before, and there may have been no need to change equipment in the intervening period. Starting up new provides a chance to be as

well equipped as they probably were years before. So many changes have come about in equipment in the last few years, now you have the opportunity to offer your clients quite a few advantages in treatment, increased comfort in epilation, comfortable couches to help both the client and yourself, improved magnification, storage, sterilization methods, etc. All these things have been designed to ease the work and improve the technique of the operator and for the client's benefit too. Why not take advantage of the new technology: the money only gets spent once and mistakes go on being regretted for years.

FINANCING YOUR BUSINESS

Setting up in business can be traumatic, and with bank loans hard to obtain, high interest rates, etc., it is useful to look at different ways to obtain finance. Unfortunately nothing is as cheap, if unpalatable, as using the hard-earned money saved from your work. Other ways are available, however, such as leasing, which for a fixed sum provides all the professional needs and gets the business underway. Most leasing is arranged through a finance house or lending source, so they will want to look at the individual's business experience, bank balance or lack of it, and assess the prospects. Loans cannot be expected without some kind of security; the finance houses are in the 'lending for gain' business, and not the 'risk' business. So it is necessary to have a good bank reference, to be well qualified, to seem business like, and to want to borrow only a sensible amount for buying or leasing equipment over a period. Then it is possible that you will get help. Leasing costs can normally be charged as an expense against income tax-wise, which is helpful, but only operates if you are bringing in sufficient income to make the costs allowable.

Buying equipment outright provides a greater feeling of security. Nevertheless it may mean the purchase has to be delayed, and this time could be spent more rewardingly by earning within a business. Only part of the capital costs of the initial setting up — equipment, clinic furniture, etc. — can be claimed against income earned as a depreciation allowance (wear and tear, and loss of overall value of goods). The investment in equipment will always be there and does not add to the recurring expenses like rent, telephone, advertising, etc., as it would if leased — so both ways of setting up have their advantages. Fit the circumstances around the situation and find the best way to get started personally. Try not to set so many expenses against the business that even if really busy, it can never be successful financially. Another few months of gaining experience and savings could reduce a lot of worries later, and enable the business to get off to a good start, capable of surviving a few lean months while the clientele builds slowly.

BUILDING A BUSINESS AND A PROFESSIONAL IMAGE

Electrology is attracting younger operators, because it is a worthwhile career, combines well with marriage and family later, and can be rewarding and interesting work. As the operators get younger, so do their clients, and these young women are less embarrassed about hair problems and more willing to come and solve them. They are more conscious about the way they look and do not hide away from the problem, but seek qualified staff to whom they can relate for a solution. So the opportunity is there for young professionals to relate very well to their younger clients' needs, and become very professional if they remember some basic rules of presenting a business-like image. Young electrologists can survive in private practice very well, and can help bring about a more modern public view of the field of electrology which should increase the client potential enormously.

Only a small proportion of people who can afford and would benefit from epilation treatment ever actually come to be helped. Why is this? Could it be that the public image of electrologists is not attractive? Or is it that people worry about coming for help because it is not a solution that appeals to them? Reasons are many, for example fear, shyness, embarrassment of revealing the extent of the problem, and a lack of common ground between the public and the profession. Electrologists or rather the profession could benefit from the services of a public relations firm to improve their popular image, and make them more approachable to the ordinary woman. It is necessary to work at creating a professional image, and contribute in any way possible to improve public awareness of the advances that have taken place in recent times in the field. The pain reduction factor, for example, benefits the potential client directly, so she needs to know about it.

In training, the student is taught management skills and how to organize a business, but in the real world it is necessary to build up a clientele. Learning how to promote the business to its best advantage is one sure way to gain new clients.

Building a business is not simply a matter of being skilful. It takes a combination of work skills and professional image to build a sound electrology practice — but that is not all there is to it. Remember all businesses need promoting — so it is important to *sell the service*. Few electrologists are without healthy competition, but at least when it is from qualified operators it is fair competition. Both operators can lose, however, if a population is only small and simply cannot sustain two professionals, and the established operator does not always come off best when a new clinic or practice opens. So shape up for competition, and be better, if not in skill at least in other ways. Give a good service,

have the latest equipment, look after your clients, provide a friendly, efficient service and you will hold your clients and build a good practice.

Think about getting the client in the first place. Apart from referrals or perhaps editorial coverage in a newspaper — which is always excellent publicity — the client may have made a choice from advertisements or the *Yellow Pages.* Convenience must be a major reason for people choosing a particular practice to come to, because it is easy to get to, or it is close to routes they normally travel. Make the advertisement clear, simple, attractive; ensure it says specifically where the practice is located, and gives your name and professional qualifications. The client must feel she is consulting an expert, and does not have to go too far out of her way to get help. Check the advertisement is correctly worded, with no errors, and says what it is supposed to: where the business is, professional details, telephone number.

Unwanted Hair? — Solve the Problem for EVER.

For a SAFE and Permanent ANSWER
to your HAIR PROBLEM
CONSULT
Your Local Institute of Electrolysis member.

MRS. B. SMITHE D.R.E.

Tel. 43-62-0919—Clinic-42
(CRN · Freemont & Brant) Freemont

Once the client has selected a clinic, she may telephone for further details. What response will she get? A sharp voice, annoyed at being interrupted while working perhaps? When busy, try to arrange for someone to answer the telephone or get an answering/recording device — although not everyone's friend it is better than a poor reply. When the call is returned, it will be with the speaker in the correct frame of mind and tone of voice to gain a client, not put one off. A reassuring and professional manner on the telephone may confirm a booking for a client, or encourage her to come to see the practice to discuss the problem she has. An explanatory leaflet can also be sent to the client if she is apprehensive about making an appointment.

Once the first appointment has been booked, the client will then see both the operator and the clinic, beauty salon or home practice, and will form an impression that will stay with her a long time, and will either gain or lose the client. Make sure that the premises look tidy and inviting, and are easy to find — if not, explain the directions carefully over the telephone or have a little map drawn inside the leaflets to send out. Nothing is more flustering to a nervous client than having trouble in finding the clinic. Make sure the client is made welcome as she enters; think

about how she may feel on her first visit to someone unknown who is going to complete a possibly uncomfortable treatment on her. Think of ways of relieving anxiety and putting the client at ease as she enters: a few kind words of conversation can pay off in terms of clients' increased pain capacity, and acceptance of the treatment. The age of the operator has nothing to do with having a caring attitude to clients, and although more mature electrologists have more life experience to equip them for the task of good client handling, younger electrologists can be equally skilled at it if they apply themselves, and think about their clients' needs in a positive way.

Consider the business location. Are there parking facilities? Is public transportation close to hand? Remember, many older clients do not drive and like to be independent. Will the business location appeal to clients? Can they combine their visit with shopping or another chore or pleasure? Make sure the address is clear, and clients know they are welcome to enter, and can feel comfortable as they wait. Is the reception clean and inviting? Are magazines and professional journals available to pass the time? Is the decor restful, likely to calm the client's nerves and make her feel more at ease? Colour can be a really great relaxer used subtly. Try not to keep the client waiting — it builds up anxiety, and is also unprofessional. If there is a reason for a delay, let the client know, so she feels taken care of and not forgotten. It is possible that she may have a small chore to see to that can be fitted in before, not after, the appointment. Remember, clients are often business professionals themselves, or have tight schedules to fit in around school and family events, so do not be discourteous and make them wait. They may find another operator who can keep to time.

So far all the pointers have led the client to the business: advertising, telephone conversation, business premises, clinic name board, comfortable outer office, welcoming reception; all necessary factors in developing a professional practice. Now the electrologist has personally to win and keep the client, and the first impression is the one that tells. Professional image and manner has never been more important and a few minutes spent putting the client at ease will pay dividends in the future. Being well-groomed, freshly but subtly made-up, with clean uniform, and most of all a pleasant approach to the person as an individual, will confirm the impression gained over the telephone — of a skilled and caring professional. This client 'bonding', even before the client has experienced the level of skill or actually seen where the work will be completed, will provide the practice with satisfied and loyal clients. With the work image matching the level of skill, the client will feel reassured of professional abilities and will relax and allow herself to be taken care of.

Quality service is always expected. The public are seeking professional staff who keep up with the latest and best in the business, so do not let the clients be more up to date than you. Let *them* know what is new, not the other way around. Be prepared to spend time, effort and money building a practice. Advertising, public relations and personal recommendations work to get people in — and good work keeps them.

PROFESSIONAL SKILLS TO KEEP CLIENTS

Always strive for excellence in the work, for even with very modest resources and surroundings it is possible to do an accurate and skilled job and provide a caring service. If the client gets the results she wants — removal of her hairs without skin damage or personal distress — she will value the skills offered, and will stay loyal. She will also make recommendations to her friends if she has been satisfied with the work.

Set the business up correctly, with a simple but efficient system of clients' records, accounting, etc., so that a complete background of the client is available to show how treatment is progressing. Use of a simple computer makes life much easier for many electrologists; this records all the clients' details, and provides information as to durations of treatments, intensities used, current combinations, etc., which ensures the exact pattern of the treatment plan and avoids errors occurring. It also provides a complete medical record to the client's condition, can record changes in the hair growth patterns — which might point out a need for more medical information or help, etc. — and can point out when treatment should not be given (contra-indications). Keeping a detailed and complete record of the clients' affairs, treatment details, payments, progress, and overall physical condition, really

shows the electrologist as not only a caring and skilled individual, but also as a successful business operator. This appeals to other professionals who appreciate the need to be up to date on all business matters. Electrology is a business like any other: the need for dedication in the work should not obscure that fact, so use all the modern tools available to offer an efficient service to the clients.

Always display diplomas with pride, and also certificates obtained from continuing education courses run at conferences, etc., as this shows the client your wish to stay up to date for her sake. Talk to the client about new advances so she is aware that you are interested in her as an individual, and want to do your best for her. Qualifications are hard earned. Be proud of them and display them to win business.

KEEPING UP TO DATE AND SUPPORTING YOUR PROFESSION

Try to keep learning, and if it is felt that knowledge and skills are lacking, go out and master them, through further education courses, advanced studies and conferences. Admitting the need or desire to learn more is the sign of a real professional.

Conferences provide wonderful opportunities to learn and exchange knowledge. They provide the ideal neutral atmosphere to look at the latest equipment, new techniques, latest thinking on techniques or the problems of hair conditions. They also provide a chance to look at the latest methods of hair removal, and to see what they have to offer. Keep informed but do not be gullible about treatment breakthroughs. Try to research the facts, ask leading questions, try the equipment out, and compare claims against personal knowledge and experience. Check the claims made against personal knowledge of anatomical and electrical information.

Treatment is advancing swiftly in terms of improved comfort and results, and it is wise to know what is happening before the client or the media gets to hear the story. There have been many false claims for 'painless' systems of permanent hair removal, so naturally everyone is rather wary, but the industry must always be on the alert for genuine advances, and take them if they offer real advantages in treatment. It is most important for you to find out about new systems before the competition does, to protect your own interests and those of your clients as well.

ROLE OF ASSOCIATIONS

Joining an association is an excellent way of gaining information, as well as getting support and making acquaintances in the field. Discussions at regional meetings are a good way of finding out all about the latest and best in the business, whether it is about

equipment, licensing, health regulations, or training standards, etc. Supporting the professional associations not only provides a means of keeping up to date with the latest developments, but their work on behalf of the profession improves consumer confidence in the service offered, and indirectly results in continued good business for the practitioner. Professional associations are influential in establishing minimum training standards, educational entry and durations and content of training — which in their turn help improve standards in the field. If public confidence is not built up in the service offered, the profession will suffer. If the work completed turns out badly, because of inadequate training opportunities and lack of background knowledge, then the profession will lose its clients and everyone suffers.

It is important to do everything possible to promote good standards, within the work itself and by example to others. Speak up if something is seen which discredits the profession — try to give the true picture and stick up for the field in which you work. Bad publicity is a very difficult thing to combat, and because of unqualified operators the profession does tend to attract a fair share of it, so wherever the opportunity arises to improve the public image, use it to advantage.

Joining and supporting a professional association works positively in many ways. It gains the friendly support of others, and by working together can achieve many things. By joining together across the country, by affiliation of the regional or state/county associations or branches, it is possible to set a national standard on such matters as training, and this standard can be confirmed by licensing controls. The process of accreditation in the United States approves training standards, recognizes the standards achieved in schools and colleges, and works towards establishing a minimum training duration that will be to the good of the profession and the public. If all states co-operate in setting and maintaining a high standard of professional training, it will help to build consumer confidence in the level of service obtained.

If, on a personal level, initial training was not thorough, and valuable time and effort has had to be spent filling in the gaps, then help to ensure new trainees receive a well-regulated, soundly based training, by pushing for accreditation or minimum training periods of at least 600 hours. In this lies future standards of excellence in the field. Confidence only comes from knowledge, so help to ensure that the trainee electrologist is given time to acquire this confidence within the training received.

PROFESSIONAL CONDUCT

Being interested in the work, and doing it well, results in a stimulating and rewarding career. Ignorance, disinterest, or apathy

about the work can only result in failure, for which there is no excuse. Knowledge and concern about the client, coupled with enthusiasm and dedication, lead to success and a prosperous business future. In any field of endeavour the main requirements for success are conviction, enthusiasm, and caring. It is necessary to be satisfied, happy and informed about the work, to have conviction and belief in its value to the individual.

Being proud of what can be accomplished with the skills acquired reflects on the clients, who need to believe that they can be helped. Then they will place their trust in the operator, and follow guidance on treatment duration and spacing to attain the desired results. Clients must be given the possibility of success and believe that it can occur through combined efforts.

BE A PROFESSIONAL

The electrologist has to be skilled, able to work quickly and well, with confidence, and must have a lively personality that does not jar on the client. She has to work to put the client at ease and help her through a trying treatment. The electrologist's job is to do the best she can for the client, regardless of her personality. With a mature and informed attitude, the operator is able to answer all the client's worries and queries. It is important to have a good working appearance that matches the level of skill offered, and to be fit and have an interested approach to the work. Being disciplined and professional helps overcome low spirits or tiredness, and thinking about the client's problems rather than your own makes each day pass swiftly. Never involve the client in your personal problems; present a professional image in a caring and sympathetic way, not an over-familiar way. It is hard not to get over-involved with the client on a personal level, but it can lead to difficulties on occasions, so take care to maintain a friendly but not over-casual relationship. Clients are in rather a fraught state when they seek help from the electrologist, so could tend to depend on the operator in too intimate a way, and must be encouraged to build their own confidence in life. Sustained support through a treatment plan is vital, if it is to be really successful.

Remember, the client has a choice, so deal with her with integrity. Honesty and trust are important attributes, so is punctuality, but most important is the skill to solve the client's hair problem. Electrologists have to be good at what they do, and know how important clients are to the profession, and how they can be won or lost by poor public image. The client provides the problem. It is up to the profession to provide the solution, with skill and integrity.

Useful Addresses

PROFESSIONAL ORGANIZATIONS AND EXAMINATION BOARDS

Further information on courses is available from the following examination boards and professional organizations:

Aestheticians' International Association Inc,
5206 McKinney, Dallas, Texas, USA

American Electrolysis Association,
Corresponding Secretary Sandi Strum, 211 Jonnet Building,
4099 William Penn Highway, Monroeville P.A. 15146, USA

Beauty Education International — Beauty Club
Ann Gallant, Forum, Stirling Road, Chichester PO19 2EN, UK

E A Ellison & Co Ltd, Brindley Road South,
Exhall, Coventry CV7 9EP, UK

Esthetic and Beauty Supply, 16 Coldwater Road, Don Mills,
Ontario M3B 1Y7, Canada Tel (416) 444 1154
There is also a Californian office, USA

British Association of Beauty Therapy and Cosmetology,
Secretary Mrs D. Parkes, Suite 5, Wolesley House,
Oriel Road, Cheltenham GL50 1TH, UK

British Association of Electrolysis,
16 Quakers Mead, Haddenham, Bucks HP17 8EB, UK

British Biosthetic Society,
2 Birkdale Drive, Bury, Greater Manchester BL8 2SG, UK

City and Guilds of London Institute,
46 Britannia Street, London WC1 9RG, UK

Le Comité Internationale D'Esthétiques et de Cosmetologie, (CIDESCO),
CIDESCO International Secretariat, PO Box 9, A1095 Vienna, Austria

Confederation of Beauty Therapy and Cosmetology,
Education Secretary Mrs B. Longhurst, 3 The Retreat, Lidwells Lane, Goudhurst, Kent, UK

Institute of Electrolysis,
251 Seymour Grove, Manchester M16 0DS, UK

International Aestheticians' Association,
2304 Monument Boulevard, Pleasant Hill, California 94523, USA

National Federation of Health and Beauty Therapists,
PO Box 36, Arundel, West Sussex BN18 0SW, UK

International Therapy Examination Council,
3 The Planes, Bridge Road, Chertsey, Surrey KT16 8LE, UK

The Northern Institute of Massage,
100 Waterloo Road, Blackpool FY4 1AW, UK

Skin Care Association of America,
16 West 57th Street, New York, NY, USA

South African Institute of Health and Beauty Therapists,
PO Box 56318, Pinegowrie 2123, South Africa

EQUIPMENT MANUFACTURERS

Ann Gallant Beauté Therapy Equipment,
Esthetic and Beauty Supply, 16 Coldwater Road, Don Mills, Ontario M3B 1Y7, Canada, Tel (416) 444 1154
There is also a Californian office, USA

Beauty Gallery Equipment by Ann Gallant,
E. A. Ellison & Co Ltd, Brindley Road South, Exhall, Coventry CV7 9EP, UK, Tel (0203) 362505

Colne Development Co Ltd,
2 Station Road, Twickenham, Middlesex, UK

Cristal (Equipment),
86 Rue Pixérécourt, 75020 Paris, France

Depilex Ltd and Slimaster Beauty Equipment Ltd,
Regent House, Dock Road, Birkenhead, Merseyside L41 1DG, UK

Electro-Medical Services,
Bermuda Road, Nuneaton, Warks, UK

George Solly Organization Ltd,
James House, Queen Street, Henley on Thames, Oxon, UK

Soltron Solarium and Sun Beds,
Josef Kratz, Vertriebsgesellschaft mbH Rottbitzer Straße 69–5340 Bad Honnef 6 Tel 02224/818-0 Telex jk 8861194

Nemectron Belmont Inc,
17 West 56th Street, New York, NY10019, USA

Silhouette International Beauty Equipment,
Kenwood Road, Reddish, Stockport, Cheshire SK5 6PH, UK

Slendertone Ltd,
12–14 Baker Street, London W1M 2HA, UK

Taylor Reeson Ltd,
96–98 Dominion Road, Worthing, Sussex, UK